SCIENTIFIC WRITING FOR

GRADUATE STUDENTS

SCIENTIFIC WRITING FOR

GRADUATE STUDENTS

A MANUAL ON THE TEACHING OF

SCIENTIFIC WRITING

EDITED BY F. PETER WOODFORD

A COUNCIL OF BIOLOGY EDITORS MANUAL

PREPARED BY THE CBE COMMITTEE ON

GRADUATE TRAINING IN SCIENTIFIC WRITING

COUNCIL OF BIOLOGY EDITORS—1981

PREFACE

*For the teachers of scientific writing
to whom this manual is addressed*

This book has been written because the members of the Council of Biology Editors, like all editors of scientific journals, are acutely aware that many scientists write badly. It is no longer the exception but the rule that scientific writing is heavy, verbose, pretentious, and dull. Considering that the scientists who produce it have received advanced university training, this is little less than shocking. We asked ourselves why these highly educated and intelligent men and women should express themselves so obscurely, so wordily, and therefore so ineffectually. Although the reasons may be complex, one contributing factor seems clear: few universities provide formal training in scientific writing, and few even encourage their students to develop a rational technique for writing scientific papers through the study of any of the excellent available textbooks.

We believe that this hiatus in university curricula should be remedied, and that formal instruction in scientific writing should form an integral part of a scientist's university training. Although for successful scientific writing a sound knowledge of English grammar and composition is necessary, it is not sufficient. The considerations involved in this kind of writing are too profound and too subtle to be satisfactorily dealt with at an elementary level, either in high school or in college. They necessitate hard thinking about the requirements of scientific proof, the logical development of scientific argument, and precision of scientific expression. For these reasons we believe that the instruction is most effectively given at a late stage of a scientist's training—in graduate school—and that it is best given by a scientist. A graduate student is also more interested than an undergraduate in learning how to write scientific prose, because not only his dissertation, but his first journal articles are in the offing. He is more easily inspired to learn from someone who is, like him, deeply concerned with scientific research than from one who is only peripherally involved.

For the most part, then, we envisage that the teaching of scientific writ-

v

ing will be undertaken by scientists who are on university faculties and who are already much occupied with other duties. We have tried to save their time by collecting in one volume the widely scattered source materials and references necessary for the preparation of a course and by providing a framework of instruction from which they can work with the minimum of preparation. Naturally, we recognize that the method of teaching advocated here is only one of many possibilities, and that any teacher worth his salt develops his own techniques, chooses his own timing, and injects his own humor and personality into his course. We hope that the brevity of our text will show that we have tried to leave room for such individual treatment and that we do not intend the course to be followed rigidly and unimaginatively.

The timing given at the beginning of most of the chapters is based on actual experience in one-hour seminar sessions with about 20 students. Of course, instructors with differently timed sessions under different circumstances can make their own interpretation of these indications. The steps in writing a journal article have been grouped into chapters (numbered 2–9) according to a logical scheme, but there is no need for the end of a session to coincide with the end of a chapter. On the contrary, sessions can be broken off at the conclusion of any of the small steps listed and described.

From the foregoing it is clear that the manual is intended primarily for use by the *teacher* of scientific writing, and is therefore different in purpose from the many textbooks of scientific writing that are meant to be used by the student himself. Nevertheless, sufficiently motivated students will be able to use this manual directly if no instructor is available.

Because we are editors of biological and biochemical journals, we have confined our attention to the characteristics, the faults, and the subject matter of the kind of writing we encounter in the literature of the life sciences. It is probable, however, that the principles here set down apply to other scientific disciplines as well, and we expect that this book will be usable, with appropriate modifications, by scientists in other fields. In our opinion, much of the nonscientific literature that comes our way is also pompous and longwinded, and perhaps some of our strictures on faults of style might be taken to heart by nonscientists, too; but we do not wish to press the point.

Perhaps a word of explanation about the arrangement of the book is necessary. A "basic" course in scientific writing is contained in Chapters 1–10; this can be given in about 12 one-hour sessions. Chapters 11–14 contain material on other topics in scientific communication and can be incorporated or added at the instructor's discretion. Although all members of the Committee have read and criticized all drafts of each chapter and endorse the final form they have taken, we have decided to indicate who has written each chapter because we each want to take responsibility for any faults the chapter may contain and to stress that some of the contents are inevitably matters of personal opinion. In particular, we emphasize that the stand we have taken about doctoral dissertations (Chapter 11) may be in conflict with the current policy of many universities. For the markedly different styles employed by the different authors we make no apology; even though we all subscribe to the same principles of scientific writing, we strongly believe that such writing need not be uniform or colorless, and we expect each author's personality to be discernible through what he writes.

Readers will notice a certain degree of overlap with remarks on writing contained in the CBE *Style Manual for Biological Journals*, composed by another Committee of the Council of Biology Editors. We have made no attempt to avoid this, nor to urge the elimination of the sections on writing from future editions of the *Style Manual*, because the two books are addressed to different audiences—the *Style Manual* to authors and editors, and the present book to teachers.

We are aware that this manual is only a start, a single step in what we believe to be the right direction: the introduction of courses of instruction in scientific writing into university graduate schools. We are sure that the book has shortcomings, but we must rely on wider experience in its application to set them right. We welcome all criticisms and suggestions from its readers that will increase the usefulness of the manual in future editions. Even if the present manual falls far short of being the perfect guide for instructors, we shall feel that its major objective will have been attained if its publication makes the academic community aware that the teaching of scientific writing is an essential element in the training of every scientist.

Council of Biology Editors' Committee on Graduate Training in Scientific Writing

Ellsworth B. Cook	Theodore Melnechuk
Edwin L. Cooper	Marcus Rosenblum
James Forbes	F. Peter Woodford

CONTENTS

ACKNOWLEDGMENTS

It is a great pleasure to acknowledge help given to the Committee by the following individuals, by virtue both of their rigorous criticism and their generous encouragement: Warren Weaver, vice-president of the Sloan Foundation and scientific communicator par excellence; John T. Edsall, ex-editor of the Journal of Biological Chemistry and professor of biochemistry at Harvard University; William A. Bayless, director of The Rockefeller University Press; Margaret Mahoney of the Carnegie Corporation, New York; Lois DeBakey, professor of scientific communication at Tulane University; E. H. Ahrens, Jr. and Bruce A. Barron, of The Rockefeller University; Dorald A. Allred of Brigham Young University; P. W. Wilson of the University of Wisconsin; and many others. The Committee was set up under the wise direction of Robert E. Gordon and has been guided throughout by his seasoned advice. Finally, we are indebted to the preliminary work of the previous CBE Committee on Graduate Training in Scientific Writing under the chairmanship of David E. Davis.

With the generous financial support of the Alfred P. Sloan Foundation, the Council of Biology Editors was able to organize a series of annual workshops, beginning in 1967, on the teaching of scientific writing and to introduce an early draft of this manual to those who were to be the pioneers in its use. We are deeply grateful for the constructive criticism we received from all the workshop participants, and particularly from L. W. Billingsley, William R. Lockhart, Robert W. Pennak, E. S. Nasset, and Juanita H. Williams.

WRITING A JOURNAL ARTICLE

1

Clearing Away the Underbrush

TIMING:

Allow about 15 minutes for this introductory material, and plan to go
well into Chapter 2 during your first session.

Most of the students who have signed up for your course will have done so
because they are afraid of and dislike writing: they have no instinctive feeling for the power and beauty of words and no gift for putting them together tellingly. They like science because it is full of experimental action
and definite, verifiable facts; writing, on the contrary, seems to be a less
exciting activity requiring intuition, for which they have small use, and
taste, for which they have no use at all.

Your first job is to convince them that *scientific* writing is an activity
they will enjoy. It demands exactly the same qualities of thought as are
needed for the rest of science: logic, clarity, and precision. A sense of
literary "rightness" is definitely not necessary (although the few who have
such a sense should not feel disadvantaged). Assure your students that if
they will only apply scientific principles to the planning, design, and
execution of scientific writing, they will surely master it. For scientific
principles are, in essence, merely guidelines for keeping thought logical,
clear, and precise; and the outstanding characteristics of successful
scientific writing are that it is logically constructed, clearly expressed, and
precisely worded.

Your students will have spent most of their university careers studying
scientific principles, and their minds have been developed, therefore, in
just the direction needed for good scientific writing. Urge them to get rid of
the notion that because they are scientists they must of necessity be inferior
writers. Quite the reverse is true, at least for the kind of writing with which
this book is concerned. At its best, such writing is straightforward, con-

crete, exact, rigorous, clearheaded, and concise. Are not these the qualities most of us associate with scientists? Are they not the qualities your students are proud to possess to a highly developed degree?

Tell them how lucky they are. Both training and inclination predispose them to succeed in scientific writing, which is the only kind they need produce. Conversely, the "literary style" they dread, and for which they are neither suited nor trained, is not called for in scientific writing. In earlier courses in English composition they may have come to loathe all considerations of imponderable taste and nuance, to detest all subtle questions of balance and rhythm, and to distrust from the bottom of their hearts the phrasemaker and all his works. Emphasize that you are not qualified to teach literary style, and that they have not been assembled to learn it. For the task in hand—scientific writing—they need only be honestly, completely, and thoroughly scientific.

Do not be tempted, however, to go a step further and rhapsodize about how easy scientific writing is. It is not. To keep to a straight and narrow path through a thicket of complex and intertwining ideas can be extremely difficult. But it is no *more* difficult than keeping a line of research straight in the face of obstructive practical difficulties and tempting byways of investigation. And it is equally important.

If your students have been recruited not by the force of attraction (the desire to write well) but by that of compulsion (the desire of others that they write well), some may be less interested in whether they *can* improve their writing than in why they *should*. Tell such students that if they go into research—academic or industrial—they will, as a matter of course, be obliged to write papers for publication, and if they express themselves badly their papers will not be accepted in reputable journals. If they do succeed in publishing—in journals with lower standards—papers that are difficult to understand or that do not present arguments and results convincingly, their work will be disregarded and their scientific abilities will go unnoticed. Most established scientists, tolerant as they are of some faults of writing, recognize that consistently poor writing either betrays the inability to think clearly or reveals an unwillingness to take the trouble to do so. If the budding scientist wants to do himself justice, therefore, he simply must learn to write as well as he thinks.

Having made these points, ask your class to name the various kinds of writing that a scientist is called upon to produce. These include a dissertation at the start of his career; progress reports and survey papers for his close colleagues; case histories, if he is a medical man; journal articles for an audience of specialists; review articles for the less specialized; book reviews to be savored by the cognoscenti; project proposals and grant applications to be judged both by his peers and by laymen; and articles for a nonscientific but informed public. He will also have to write when he prepares talks for various types of audience. Stress that the good writer is like a well-mannered man: he is considerate of others. He must know who his readers or listeners are and aim, with this knowledge in mind, for the most rapid and comfortable communication possible.

Remind your students that writing is not extrinsic to research: it is inevitably a part of it, since research is not complete until it is published. At the same time you should, perhaps, reassure them by saying that although the first paper is notoriously the most difficult, you hope to take the sting out of even that most traumatic experience.

In this manual we suggest that you teach scientific writing not by enunciating abstract principles but, more concretely, by showing your class how to write a journal article. If you teach the course in this way, the major assignment will require the students to write up some portion of their recent or current research in the form of a journal article. Tell them this in the first session so that they may select a suitable set of experimental results by the time you next meet with them. The program presupposes that your students already have a year or more of research experience, and indeed we believe that this is the earliest stage at which students can profit from the kind of training described here. If the assignment suggested is impossible or inappropriate for your students, the "Notes on Major Assignment," p. 14, may help you to modify it.

The same belief in concreteness has led us to the piece of advice given at the head of this chapter: keep the introductory material short and get on to the steps in Chapter 2 within your first session. Those who have come unwillingly or skeptically to sample your course will not be won over by abstract argument about the importance of writing, but will almost certainly be intrigued by the first steps, especially the discussion of "What Is the Most Suitable Journal?", and will come back for more. Eager students will already be convinced that they want to improve their writing, and will be impatient to begin.

The instruction on the journal article (Chapters 2–8) has been designed according to the cardinal principle of Logic Before Language. There is a great deal more to writing an article than arranging well-chosen words in a clear, concise way. Before you introduce the dread word Style you must dwell long and thoroughly on how to define and delimit a topic, how to select some and exclude other experimental results, how to group ideas, how to arrange tables and figures, and how to write an outline. Some of these topics will be familiar to you from general treatises on writing; others are relevant to scientific writing only, and even for the more general topics many of the approaches suggested here for teaching them are unorthodox.

The order in which the topics are dealt with has been deliberately designed for palatability to the scientist. He is interested primarily in logical connections, so talk about logic and organization first. No one will be surprised as you develop the theme that only logical reasoning can produce a satisfying structure for the article. Then, when you have your students' full confidence, lead them gradually to the realization that the *same kind* of logical reasoning can yield precision and clarity in each sentence of the finished manuscript. In this way they will come, via paths that appeal to them, to an interest in words and their relationships. They will come to recognize that words are the coin in which we exchange thought, and that discussion of words in this context constitutes not a literary exercise, but a truly scientific activity.

2
The Ground Plan

YOU WILL NEED:

Copies of a few leading journals, some of wide scope (e.g., *Science, Nature, Journal of Biological Chemistry*), some of greater specialization (any high-quality subspecialty journals appropriate to your class). Choose the issues containing the Instructions to Authors or obtain copies of these for each journal.

One or two copies of *Current Contents* (Institute for Scientific Information, Philadelphia, Pa.).

Trelease, Sam F. 1958. *How to Write Scientific and Technical Papers.* Williams and Wilkins Co., Baltimore. (Paperback edition: The M.I.T. Press, Cambridge, Mass., 1969.) Recommend this as a textbook that deals best with logical considerations in scientific writing. Of the many books on this subject that are in print, this is by far the pithiest, the most profound, and above all the most scientific. It is not surprising to discover that it was written by a scientist. All page numbers in Trelease given in later chapters of this manual refer to the 1958 hard-cover edition.

Since Trelease's own writing is highly condensed, students may find it a little indigestible if read at a sitting. A good plan is, therefore, to send them to the relevant passage only after you have expounded it vividly, with examples, in class.

YOU SHOULD READ:

Rosenblum, M. 1965. "Information Handling for the Biomedical Sciences." In *A National Program to Conquer Heart Disease, Cancer and Stroke.* U.S. Govt. Printing Office, Washington, D.C. 20402. 2:410–437.

Biological Sciences Curriculum Study. 1965. *Biological Science: Interaction of Experiments and Ideas.* Prentice-Hall, Inc., Englewood Cliffs, N.J. 77–97.

TIMING:

With Chapter 1, this chapter up to the end of Step 3 (including discussion) takes one hour.

Assignments:

Writing an abstract of a major article in a field appropriate to the students' interests. It is desirable to select an article that has either an unsatisfactory published abstract or no abstract at all.

Obtaining the Instructions to Authors (containing "Purpose and Scope") for a journal of the student's choice.

Any complex, large-scale task, which may be overwhelming to the beginner in its entirety, becomes more manageable when broken down into parts. The task of writing a journal article has therefore been broken down into about two dozen small steps, each of them rather quickly completed, which are described in this and subsequent chapters. Obviously, you may wish to increase this number, to skip lightly over some steps, or to rearrange them according to your own experience. They are listed in Table 1, page 9.

Stress the Two-Way Relationship Between Thinking and Writing

As you will inevitably find yourself constantly returning to one principle throughout the course, it might as well be discussed at the outset. It is that thinking and writing mutually interact. Good scientific writing is, of course, impossible without clear thinking. What is less obvious and less widely appreciated is that careful writing can actually assist in developing logical scientific thought. Somehow the discipline of crystallizing a thought into a grammatical sentence with a beginning, a middle, and an end clarifies, sharpens, and delimits that thought. You will find ample opportunity to demonstrate this useful feedback effect of writing (see, for example, Steps 2 and 5 below), and will be astonished how rapidly your students' power of clear, precise thinking will develop as they utilize it.

Several of the steps, including the first four, take the form of questions that the student is to ask himself.

STEP 1:   What Is the Right Time to Publish?

Graduate students who have not yet published find this an unexpected question. All the better, for one cannot impress upon them too early or too forcibly that good reasons must be given before they add a single drop to the flood of publication. Some scientists seem to believe that the world will be perpetually grateful to them for keeping what amounts to a public diary

TABLE 1   *Steps in Writing a Journal Article*

Step	Title	Page
1	What is the right time to publish?	8
2	What question has been asked, and what are the conclusions?	10
3	What is the most suitable journal?	12
4	How are the findings related to the existing body of knowledge?	14
5	Write the title and synopsis	15
6	Reread the "Purpose and Scope" in the chosen journal	16
7	Read the Instructions to Authors	16
8	Decide on the basic form of the article	17
9	Stock the section reservoirs	18
10	Construct the tables and figures	19
11	Construct the topic outline	20
12	Construct the sentence outline	21
13	Think of the article as a unit; write the first draft continuously from beginning to end	23
14	The Introduction: keep it short	24
15	Construct the list of references as you go along	25
16	Materials and Methods section(s): include the right amount of detail	26
17	Results section: allow the data to speak for themselves	28
18	Discussion section: watch for symptoms of megalomania	29
19	Are major alterations necessary?	30
20	Polishing the style	33, 34
21	Give drawings to Illustration Department	104
22	Write title and abstract in final form	104
23	Reread the journal's instructions to authors before having the manuscript typed	106
24	Departmental review	107
25	Shelve the manuscript for a while	108

of their diligent activity, or endlessly titillated by accounts of their violations of each one of Nature's infinite number of maidenheads. Science does not advance by the accumulation of facts gathered at random and published with the fatuous justification that they may "shed light" on some as yet nonexistent problem. Make the idea of such publication repugnant to your class. If you suspect that they may be more moved by considerations of ambition than of altruism, stress that in the councils whose opinions really matter in the furtherance of their careers, a few good papers count for far more than an infinitude of shameful "potboilers."

Actual evidence of the unfavorable effects of rushing into print is presented in Allen's article "Why Are Research Grant Applications Disapproved?" (Allen, E. M. 1960. *Science*. 132: 1532), which reveals that 12.6 per cent of the rejected proposals in the sample examined were disapproved because the investigator's previously published work did not inspire confidence. Let your students weigh this against the witty but oversimplified catchphrase "Publish or perish," by which they are all too easily impressed. Remind them that the printed word is indelible and that, even in the face of pressure from superiors, their first duty is to safeguard their future reputations. You will, of course, give special and different consideration to the rare, reticent creature who actually must be encouraged to publish his excellent research.

Well, what *is* the right moment to publish? Ideally, when a research question of some importance has been asked and a convincing answer found. Sometimes the complete answer cannot be expected within five or ten years; then publication is justified when a sizable step toward that answer has been taken. Perhaps the best criterion is: has a significant advance in knowledge been made? Remind the members of your class that on this point they will have to satisfy not only their own consciences but also a group of critics who may be even sterner: the editors, editorial board, and reviewers of the scientific journal to which the article is submitted. A young scientist's first contact with publishing can be a shattering experience; try to transform it into an educational one by preparing him for the cold-eyed appraisal of his peers. More on the kind of preparation to provide is given in Chapter 9.

STEP 2: *What Question Has Been Asked, and What Are the Conclusions?*

Step 1 has been occupied with pondering these questions, and now we apply the device of writing down the answers in order to tether the thoughts to solid ground. The device establishes exactly what the article will be about. Failure to do this leads to the kind of publication that is, alas, only too frequent—the one that impels the exasperated reader to ask "What on earth is the man driving at?" Furthermore, the written sentences define the article's limits. Frequently the researcher is occupied with a number of closely related questions. It is imperative that he decide *which* question or questions will be discussed; which data are relevant, therefore, and which must be excluded.

Emphasize especially the form of the heading of this section: "What question has been asked?" (or alternatively, "What hypothesis has been examined?"), not "What was the purpose of the research?" The latter question can lead to the formless "purpose" of "investigating such-and-such a process" or "gathering data concerned with such-and-such a phenomenon," which advances nobody in the pursuit of explicitness and definition.

> ASSIGNMENT You can help your students read, as well as write, more effectively if you encourage them to ask "What was the question, and what are the conclusions?" of every article they study. Your first assignment can give them practice in this—and simultaneously convey that this course is concerned more with scientific thinking than with niceties of literary style—if it consists in having them make an abstract of a published paper. To convey the full meaning and significance of a major paper in a stringently limited number of words (say between 100 and 200) constitutes a challenging intellectual exercise. Usually you will be able to select a paper that will be sufficiently comprehensible, for the purposes of the exercise, to all members of the class. A list of well-written articles in several biological fields is given in *BioScience*, 1964, 14:22–23. Perhaps the students should aim at improving on the informativeness of the published abstract, where there is one, in a version that is only two-thirds as long. The assignment should be completed before the second class meets.
>
> Much fruitful discussion can arise out of this assignment. Students are eager to exercise their critical judgment, and will come up with many (real or imagined) faults of omission and commission even in a fairly good article. Encourage them to turn this critical faculty on their own writing and to resolve never to commit these faults when their turn comes to publish. You will almost certainly find instances in which the students have misread the article. Sort out with them who was at fault—they or the author—and stress the importance of critical, *accurate* reading. You can, perhaps, circulate your own version of the abstract and ask them to improve upon it.
>
> Alternatively, you may choose not to comment on this assignment in detail, but to give the same assignment at the end of the course

in order to assess (and have the students judge for themselves) what progress has been made in critical reading and thinking, as well as in writing, as a result of the course.

STEP 3:   *What Is the Most Suitable Journal?*

With the precise knowledge of the contents and scope of the proposed article gained in Step 2, the author is ready to consider where he will submit it. I realize that the advice to consider this question so early is unorthodox. Yet it is a commonplace that the effectiveness of any piece of writing is directly related to the writer's knowledge of the audience to whom it is addressed. Nothing is more discouraging, demoralizing, and time-wasting than to prepare an article for a journal that rejects it for inappropriateness of content. Conversely, nothing saves more time at every stage of the article's preparation than the clear knowledge of where it will be submitted and who is likely to read it.

> ASSIGNMENT Point out that all journals publish a statement of their purpose and scope, although not necessarily in every issue. Have your students name the journal in which they expect to publish their next (or first) article and require them to obtain and study the "purpose and scope" of that journal and of possible alternatives before embarking on their Major Assignment.

Ask your students by what criteria they would choose one journal over another. You will elicit (or may have to supply) such answers as the following, and can expand them by means of the questions in parentheses.

1. General quality and prestige. (How is this judged? Does the composition of the editorial board provide a clue? What are your supervisor's and colleagues' opinions? Can you judge by critical appraisal of the contents?)
2. Size of audience. (A statement of circulation appears annually in most U.S. journals; those that carry advertising usually have a circulation of 5,000 or more.)
3. Type of audience. (Are you interested in reaching specialists only, or a wide audience? Is this determined solely by the journal, or do present methods of scanning lists of titles and selecting articles from *any* journal make this consideration unimportant?)
4. Speed of publication. Point out the distinction between date of *receipt*

of manuscripts by a journal and the date of their *acceptance* for publication. Many journals publish both dates, from which one can deduce the time taken for the editorial process, including any necessary revision by the author; further, by comparing the date of acceptance with the date of publication of the issue one can deduce the time taken for the "production" phase—composition, proofreading, printing, and binding.

5. Quality of photographic reproduction. (In what types of work is this important?)

At this juncture it is useful to review and expand the students' knowledge of primary journals and of their place in the whole scientific information process. Such knowledge facilitates students' use of the literature and of the library at all stages of their work. It also enables them to write a primary journal article more intelligently, because they are aware that it is the fundamental unit of scientific communication, which is built into a more complex system by several means (publication of the abstract, discussion in other journal articles, citation in reviews, incorporation into textbooks). Excellent background for your handling of this subject is Rosenblum's source paper on the biomedical information system (see the beginning of this chapter). Your students should read the section "Guides to the Literature" in Trelease's book, pp. 11–25. The elementary but exceptionally clear description of the scientific literature in *Biological Science: Interaction of Experiments and Ideas* (see beginning of this chapter) may suggest some questions to test your students' knowledge, and your own experience will supply others. What do they think are the criteria by which submitted manuscripts are judged? (In general, these include relevance to the journal's field, importance of the questions asked and the conclusions reached, strength of the experimental evidence, and clarity of presentation.) Do journals differ in the strictness with which they apply the criteria? What other considerations might be of overriding importance?

You can pull this discussion together, perhaps, by a practical suggestion for seeking a suitable journal in which to publish: scanning of *Current Contents*. The names of journals listed at the front of that publication will suggest that some of them should be examined further; since the titles of articles appearing in the current issue of those journals are reproduced inside, this can be conveniently done without extensive search in the library.

Notes on Major Assignment

It is unlikely that every member of your class has material ready to be published when your course begins. Encourage those who are not so far along either to select a small group of experiments, which is complete but which they would not normally consider (Step 1) a sufficiently important advance in knowledge to publish as a full paper; or to choose a portion of the work in progress that is incomplete, but for which a probable result can be predicted arbitrarily and appropriate conclusions drawn. The less artificial the exercise is, of course, the more effective it will be, but there need be nothing artificial about the second alternative I have described; in many types of experiments the experimenter knows beforehand that result A must lead to one conclusion and result B to another. Another possibility is to make the major assignment the description of a research proposal (see Chapter 12) concerned with work the student is embarking upon. Your important task is to ensure that the subject matter of the major assignment is research with which the student is personally involved.

Offer to discuss the choice of material for the assignment if the students have any difficulty in selecting it. Make sure that the choice is made early in the course and that the projected paper is small in scope, otherwise the student will have great difficulty keeping up with the steps as they are discussed in class. Once the material has been chosen, the student will require three weeks to complete Steps 1–12, when he will be ready to submit to you his sentence outline (see p. 21).

S T E P   4 :   *How Are the Findings Related to the Existing Body of Knowledge?*

Once again, this is a step in which the author writes down what is presumably already fairly clear in his mind in order to clarify it further. What he writes specifies the *exact* area in which his advance has been made, where the work of others stopped short, and what the future developments could be. It eliminates irrelevant aspects of the field and prepares the ground for the Introduction and Discussion sections. Emphasize how precise you want this piece of thinking to be: one describes not the whole jigsaw puzzle of (say) amino acid metabolism, but only the pieces immediately surrounding the new knowledge concerning aspartate oxidation that is now to be fitted in.

STEP 5: *Write the Title and Synopsis*

What a surprising piece of advice, your students will exclaim. People usually tell us to devise the title last! Furthermore, as to the synopsis, how can we give a general view of something that is not yet written? Explain that this is another piece of writing to clarify thinking. Although the title may well have to be revised when the article is finished, and the synopsis will almost certainly have to undergo a transformation before it can serve as an abstract, writing both of them at this point is invaluable to the author who is aiming for a tightly constructed article that is free from all irrelevance. And the student is, in fact, already perfectly well equipped to produce a working title and synopsis. He has a clear idea of what he has to say (Step 2), how it relates to previous knowledge (Step 4), and what constitutes his experimental evidence (in his notebooks); he is therefore in an excellent position to expound his projected paper in definite and concise terms, as though to a friend who asks him at some chilly street corner what he has been up to recently. The synopsis should be a logical chain of reasoning ("What was the question?"), observation ("What is the evidence?"), and deduction ("What are the conclusions?") without a single weak link in it. The author really defines the subject of his article and the limits he has set for it only when he has written a satisfactory title and synopsis. When this is done, he can feel that he has properly pegged out his ground plan and is free to move about comfortably within its well-defined limits as he plans the article in more detail and proceeds to its construction.

3

The Master Plan

YOU WILL NEED:

Copies of the Instructions to Authors in journals you deem appropriate.

TIMING:

Together with the last two steps in Chapter 2, a full hour.

ASSIGNMENT:

Steps 1–5 of the student's journal article (Major Assignment). Possibly, the reduction of a published article to outline form.

STEP 6: *Reread the "Purpose and Scope" in the Chosen Journal*

Now, with the subject matter firmly delineated on paper in the form of title and synopsis, the student should match it once more against the subject area of the journal he has chosen. This is his last chance to change his mind about the journal, for from here on all his words will be directed to that journal and to its readers. Because every line of communication has a receiving end as well as a transmitter, the successful writer is acutely aware of his audience. He must often decide, for example, "Should I explain this, or will my readers know it so well that they will be irritated by an explanation? On the other hand, can I find two or three words to bring in the less well-informed or less specialized reader without antagonizing the more sophisticated?" Such questions of judgment can be decided only if the student knows who his readers are likely to be. Study of the "Purpose and Scope" will aid his intelligent guesswork in that direction.

STEP 7: *Read the Instructions to Authors*

Ask your students what sort of information is contained in the Instructions to Authors that appear in most journals. Much of it is concerned with such mechanical matters as the number of copies to be submitted, spacing of lines, treatment of footnotes, etc., which will become important to the student only later. Nevertheless, even at this stage, it is necessary to know such things as whether there is a page limit (as in, for example, *Proc. Nat. Acad. Sci. U.S.* and *J. Exp. Med.*); whether any style manual or other standard is adhered to for abbreviations; whether there are any special rules on nomenclature; and so on. Much time and patience can be needlessly expended on these matters if they are ignored until a later stage.

STEP 8: *Decide on the Basic Form of the Article*

Most scientific articles, at least in the life sciences, are arranged in four main sections: (a) Introduction, (b) Materials and Methods, (c) Results, and (d) Discussion. There are those who deplore this standardization, either because all uniformity is deadening or because it gives a false impression of an unimaginatively logical approach to scientific questions. Yet no one has authoritatively laid down this form; it evolved, early in the twentieth century, as scientific publication became more voluminous. It represents, I submit, a survival of the fittest among the various possible forms, where "fittest" means the most streamlined and efficient means of conveying information. It should be discarded, then, only when circumstances are absolutely compelling.

Obviously, material should not be forced into this mold when it does not fit—for example, a theoretical treatment of previously published results or a piece of work in which the reader must know the results of one portion before being introduced to the methods and experimental design of another. But the best advice to students is: use the conventional form whenever possible; if you adopt another one, do it in the conscious knowledge that some proved advantages of the conventional form will inevitably be lost, and satisfy yourself that there will be a net gain *beyond* the satisfaction of being unorthodox.

This is a good point at which to discuss the advantages of combining the Results and Discussion sections, together with the dangers. Any special forms, such as taxonomic descriptions, that are of special interest to your students should, of course, also be examined critically. You may also like to comment on how the Methods section has moved, at least in biochemical journals, from its former position as a sort of necessary appendix at the end of a paper to its present prominence near the beginning, and to explore the

reasons. One is that the type of methods employed and the purity of substances used often have a profound effect on the results and on their interpretation. So important is this information that a further subdivision of
the experimental section may become necessary, into a section headed
"Materials" (in which the sources of both chemicals and biological tissue
are stated and their purity is discussed) and another section headed
"Methods."

In what follows, I have assumed that the conventional form has been
adopted, but I do not mean to imply that no other is possible.

STEP 9:   *Stock the Section Reservoirs*

A fundamental mistake of the inexperienced writer is to sit down with a
rough mental outline of what he has to say, seize a pen with desperation
and a groan, and start writing. At the end of the first page of botched sentences and confused thoughts, he is, not unnaturally, discouraged; only by
great effort of will can he return to that distasteful pursuit—writing—and
make another attempt.

It will by now have become apparent that this method is not the one
advocated in this course. Because those scientists who are not "born
writers" have no inherent pleasure in constructing a balanced sentence or a
well-turned phrase, they should concentrate first on the things they do
enjoy: facts, ideas, and logical connections. Tell your students, therefore,
to take five sheets of paper; head them Introduction, Materials and Methods, Results, Discussion, and References; and into these reservoirs put—in
any order they like—brief indications of facts, experiments, thoughts, and
observations that belong in each. Naturally, the student's notebooks,
graphs, card index, etc., should all be at hand to refresh his memory. The
following considerations should influence his decisions on the items that
are being added to the reservoirs:

(a) Is the item necessary? This is decided by reference to the title
and synopsis, constructed in Step 5.

(b) In what section does the item belong? Some items may seem to
have connections with two sections or even more; such items should be
prominently marked, and the writer should consider carefully at this stage
where they will be developed in most detail.

(c) Are all necessary items included?

As the work on the reservoirs continues, the structure of each section *and its relationship to the other sections* begin to emerge. More than one possible structure for the article may suggest itself, and if the student numbers the items he can readily experiment with different logical arrangements. But before the topic outline is attempted, another extremely important step must be completed.

STEP 10: *Construct the Tables and Figures*

The student will protest that he has already tabulated his data and drawn his graphs; this was how he knew that he was ready to publish (Step 1). Explain to him that he is now going to draw them up in a way that will be completely intelligible to others. This includes composing full titles and footnotes for the tables as well as legends for the figures and labels for the axes of graphs. The step has three objects.

First, if tables are cleverly designed and have informative titles and complete footnotes, and if figures can be comprehended at a glance and have intelligible legends, the reader can glean not only the results but also a great part of the experimental design without any reference to the text. In the final paper the tables and figures, together with the title and the abstract, should form a coherent story. Ask your students in what order they look at the various parts of a published article, and many of them will give you: title, abstract, figures, tables, introduction, discussion, results, methods. Now, if it is true that figures and tables are often examined before the text, they should not be dependent on the text for comprehensibility. Few authors seem to realize this; put your students among those few by training them to design tables and figures *in full* before a word of the text is written. The first object of this step is, then, to make tables and figures fully informative in themselves and to banish from their vicinity the irritating and usually unnecessary inscription "see text."

Second, the tables and figures give the author a sort of extended synopsis of the paper. This may modify ideas developed in Step 9 as to the best order of presentation and therefore be useful for the writing of the topic outline, Step 11.

Third, matching the data thus tabulated and graphed against the items in the Section Reservoirs will reveal whether the conclusions must be modified (or abandoned!) and whether more experimental work should be done before the work is ripe for publication. In either of these two cases, time will not be wasted in writing a paper that may never see the light of day or that will reflect no credit on the author if it does.

These points about tables and figures are further elaborated in Chapter 10, but I think they are best discussed in detail after the students have already made mistakes and scored successes in designing tables and figures in the course of writing their major assignment.

Class discussion of Step 10 and its purposes will bring home to the students how useful it is to begin "writing" a journal article (using Steps 1–10) when a piece of research is *nearing* completion instead of when it seems to be finished. The steps reveal more concretely than vague daydreaming just what further evidence remains to be garnered. Recommend this to your students as a useful technique of research.

STEP 11: *Construct the Topic Outline*

Let us assume that all is well and that further experimental work seems unnecessary. Now, I think, the author will be straining at the bit to put the items down in logical order—for it is really exciting to see the paper assume definite and logical form in the mind's eye. I defy anyone who is the least interested in his results to be untouched by this excitement as all the items in his reservoirs, tables, and figures seem to be jostling one another in eagerness to be put in place.

The topics should be arranged, within each section, in a logical order. What does this mean? Obviously, many different things. In Methods, perhaps a chronological handling of samples; in Results, the most important and explicable findings first, less clearcut differences later, or a gradation from simple to complex systems, or a discussion organ by organ, chemical class by chemical class; and so on. Some of these possibilities will be touched upon in subsequent steps, but, in general, scientists are strong in and proud of their logical thinking, and your students should be encouraged to display their prowess to the full. Point out the usefulness of headings, subheadings, and sub-subheadings as initial guides in writing even if they are scrapped in the final version; and stress how important it is to ensure that the ranking is logically correct, i.e., that a topic given a heading is really on the same level of importance as another that has been assigned a heading of the same magnitude. The longer the article, the more need there is for subheadings to guide both author and reader. You might add, parenthetically, that the doctoral dissertation must be strictly ordered by means of them, and that erroneous ranking is one of the major sources of confusion both in expository writing and in thinking.

The writer should make certain that he has included in his topic outline everything that was in his reservoirs and that repetition has been eliminated or minimized before he goes on to expand this outline in the next step.

STEP 12: *Construct the Sentence Outline*

Not all writers agree that a sentence outline is necessary, but its construction can be a further aid in clarifying thought for the neophyte. "How does it differ from a topic outline?" the students (rather to my surprise) ask. Whereas the topic outline defines what subject will be discussed in each section or paragraph, the sentence outline expresses what the writer has to say about that subject. Ideally, each sentence summarizes one paragraph in the finished article—shorn, of course, of all detail and supporting arguments—and the succession of sentences should make some sense to another person (allowing for the fact that transitional sentences may be necessary for complete intelligibility).

A sentence outline confers many benefits. It may, for instance, reveal gaps in the logic, even though the topic outline seemed perfect: perhaps a new heading should be inserted or the material rearranged. Sentences in the outline sometimes turn out to be so informative and pithy that the author delightedly extracts them bodily and uses them as key sentences in paragraphs of the final article. Finally, the construction of sentences prepares the writer for the phase of more continuous writing that is to come. Despite all these potential benefits, however, some writers find the sentence outline cumbersome and constricting. I ask my students to try it out experimentally, but not to force themselves to use it if it does not seem to help.

ASSIGNMENT Description of these steps goes more quickly than their execution, and your students will be ready at this stage to tackle only the Ground Plan on their major assignment. I suggest that you give them three weeks in all to reach Step 12 (first week, Steps 1–5; second week, Steps 6–10; third week, Steps 11 and 12). Only at Step 12 is it meaningful for you to examine their work (a Topic Outline is virtually incomprehensible to anyone but its author). In my experience, science students perform well in the "outline" assignments, and for this reason you may like to bolster their confidence by giving them an additional one to prepare. Ask them to take a published article (perhaps the one they have already abstracted at Step 2) and break it down into topic and sentence outlines.

You will realize that this assignment, like the abstracting one, is just the reverse of composing something as a *preparation* for writing a full text. Like a chemical compound, writing is more fully understood after it has been both analyzed and synthesized than after either analysis or synthesis alone.

4

The First Draft

YOU WILL NEED:

Copies of a good Introduction to hand out: either the one given on p. 25 or one of your own choosing.

Copies of a description of experimental methods, to be condensed into a form suitable for journal publication.

YOU SHOULD READ:

Trelease, pp. 36–42.

Gensler, W. J., and K. D. Gensler. 1961. *Writing Guide for Chemists.* McGraw-Hill, New York. Chapters 4 and 5.

TIMING:

About 1½ one-hour sessions.

ASSIGNMENTS:

Condensation of a description of experimental methods.
Steps 6 10 of the student's journal article.

STEP 13: *Think of the Article as a Unit; Write the First Draft Continuously from Beginning to End*

A prime object of good style is unity. Unity should not be difficult to achieve in a journal article, written as it is around a single theme or research problem. If you know what you have to say, the article will flow best and be most coherent if it is written with one swing from beginning to end. Of course, *no* writer can achieve perfection as he goes along: the precise word, the clinching phrase are not at one's beck and call—sometimes, in the heat of composition, one cannot even decide how to end a sentence grammatically, let alone tellingly! But such obstacles should not deter the writer of a first draft. He should plunge forward, intent on the mainstream of his message, comforting himself with the thought that careful revision will smooth out the rough passages. In later drafts, the passage may be jettisoned altogether—why streamline something you will throw away? The main objective should be to get down some sort of account of each of the essential points, in the order indicated by the Sentence Outline. Some steering aids are offered in the following steps, which give specific help in different sections of the journal article.

Sometimes the reluctant writer is advised differently. He is encouraged to tackle the easiest sections first, complete them, and experience the satisfaction of having them safely under his belt. But the easiest sections are undoubtedly the Methods and Results, and as these are preceded only by a short Introduction, which serves to orient the writer as well as the reader, I believe that this advice is not so different from mine after all. The danger of writing separately conceived sections is that of producing a "patchwork quilt" of unrelated parts that no amount of patient stitching will unify.

Most of this advice applies exclusively to short articles with a single theme, such as will be forthcoming from your students at this stage. Long articles are perforce written in several sessions, but if the student has acquired the habit of writing his first drafts quickly, without editing, he stands a better chance of reducing the number of those days when writing goes painfully and unsatisfactorily. He will be relying on a *method* and not on inspiration.

STEP 14: *The Introduction*

The key direction to give here is: *keep it short*. Some scientists deplore the disappearance of the scholarly historical introduction from scientific articles. Certainly the young scientist's frequent lack of historical perspective may be partly due to the brevity of most present-day introductions—and this may be a good moment to disabuse your students' minds of the notion that science began ten years ago. But most readers, and certainly all editors, have tired of the lengthy account of the glorious advances of the past, to which the author's modest contribution seems to be attached in the hope of gaining luster by association. With the proliferation of review articles, the necessity for an extensive introductory survey has passed. The writer must, of course, know the history of his subject thoroughly, but his knowledge will be revealed by the way he describes his own work; there is no need to demonstrate it in any other way. He should select from that knowledge just enough to orient the reader adequately and to place the work to be described in appropriate perspective.

Good introductions often fall into three parts, be they sentences or paragraphs. The first states the general field of interest. The second presents, in main lines only, the findings of others that will be challenged or developed. The third specifies the question to which the present paper is addressed. The third part may indicate by what means the question has been examined, especially if the methods are new or unfamiliar, and may or may not state the conclusions, as the author wishes. The aim throughout should be to excite and interest, not bore, the reader, and answer the question: "Why was this work embarked upon?"

Choose one or two good Introductions to distribute and discuss. Here is one (Dobbing, J. 1963. "The Entry of Cholesterol into Rat Brain During Development." *J. Neurochem.* 10:739. Reproduced by permission of the author and of Pergamon Press).

"Previous experiments have shown a remarkable persistence of cholesterol laid down at the time of myelination in the chick and rabbit brain. In these experiments cholesterol-4-^{14}C was injected into the yolk sac of day-old chicks and intraperitoneally into 17-day-old rabbits (1, 2). It was recovered from the brain up to one year later, labeled in the same place in the molecule and at no other (3).

"An incidental finding was that the cholesterol molecule itself could enter the developing brain, although brain cholesterol has hitherto been considered to be entirely derived from synthesis within the organ. This new finding has recently been challenged in experiments with rats (4).

"In the present work rats have again been used in case there should be an unexpected species difference. The experiments were undertaken to determine (a) whether cholesterol as such could enter the brain; and if so (b) whether its rate of entry was as dependent on the timing of myelination as is the entry of other myelin-sheath constituents and their precursors."

STEP 15: *Construct the List of References As You Go Along*

This piece of advice can be interjected here because the student is now actually writing the text of his article, albeit only in first draft. An unfortunately common practice is to mutter "I shall refer here to that article of so-and-so's in 1963" and to leave the "library work" to the very end. I have seen this cause more anguish than it is possible to describe. With the deadline for submission of the article two days away, the distracted author finds that half the necessary volumes are lost, borrowed, or at the bindery. All this is avoided if the writer, every time he refers to others' work, makes sure that he has the necessary reference in his files. Then, as soon as the momentum of his writing slackens, he must put down on a separate sheet, headed References, the full bibliographic details with all the authors' names, initials, and so on (is the title also required by the journal?), *in the style adopted by the journal of choice*. The references can be renumbered and rearranged later, if necessary, and their accuracy can be checked at any time, without panic, by consultation of the original in the library as the first draft nears its completion. Emphasize the importance of absolute accuracy, and make sure that your students know what the essential constituents of a reference are, namely:

For a journal reference: all authors with initials, journal title appropriately abbreviated (as recommended by the U. S. A. Standards Institute; see *Biological Abstracts*. 48 (24), 15 December 1967), volume, year, initial page (some journals require inclusive pagination), sometimes title of article. For books: author(s) with initials, title of book, editor(s) if any, number of the edition if applicable, publisher, city and year of publication, volume number if necessary, page number or inclusive pagination.

STEP 16: *Materials and Methods Section(s)*

The editors of some journals dislike, as I do, the word "Experimental" as a section heading. In no other circumstances is an adjective used as a heading, so why here? Most journals will accept the more specific heading Materials and Methods, even if their usual custom is to use the unfortunate "Experimental."

Common sense dictates when Materials and Methods should be described in separate sections, for example when the materials used are numerous and their purification is complex or particularly important. When experimental animals are used, the species and strain should be specified accurately. "Monkey" is an insufficient description in a scientific article.

Considerable delicacy of judgment is required to decide exactly how much information should be offered in the Materials and Methods section. All scientists are agreed on the principle that sufficient detail must be provided to permit the reader to repeat the experiments if he wants to. However, we must define carefully who "the reader" is. For these purposes, he must be assumed to be a trained investigator with considerable experience; otherwise, the article will become intolerably long and begin to resemble a manual of laboratory practice. The writer should ask himself constantly: "Is the average reader who is likely to want to do this work already familiar with this kind of manipulation? Are these details essential to the success of the experiment?" That the author may make the wrong decision on such questions does not absolve him from asking them and giving the best answer he can. Train your students to *include the right amount of detail.*

Apart from this, the Methods section is an easy one. The logical sequence has already been decided in the Outlines. It often follows a chronological pattern, e.g., chemical reaction conditions—purification of the product—analysis; or, treatment of animals—dissection of tissues—incubation conditions—assays—statistical methods for examination of results. Sometimes a succession of techniques, such as different types of chromatography, can form the different subheadings. Warn your students, however, of the perils of this approach if it conflicts with a chronological description, and point out how confusing it is to describe the analysis of a mixture which has yet to be extracted, or measurements on a substance of which the purification has yet to be described.

A frequent question is: "If I have used someone else's method for doing something, should I describe it or merely give a reference?" I believe that, unless the method is widely familiar (such as the method of Lowry, Rosebrough, Farr, and Randall for protein determination), the reader always appreciates being told at least the principle on which the method is based. Similarly, if the author has modified the method quoted he should give at least the outline of the modification. Modifications too trivial to be described are also too trivial to be mentioned.

> ASSIGNMENT Practice in exercising judgment about what to include and what to leave out when writing the Methods section can be provided in the following assignment, which also brings out a potentially useful distinction between the traditional "dissertation style" and that of a journal (see, however, Chapter 11). Ask your students to

condense the methods section of a dissertation to which you have access into a form suitable for a journal article. Good examples of this exercise in the field of preparative organic chemistry, in extended and condensed form, are given in Gensler and Gensler (see bibliography at the head of this chapter).

You may like to explore one technique for stimulating fruitful discussion of this assignment. Divide the class into groups of about five students and have them select and defend to the rest of the class what they consider to be the best condensed version. The critical analysis that is required brings home vividly the strengths and weaknesses of the version selected.

STEP 17: *Results Section*

The Results section should also be an easy one. The commonest fault here is to repeat in tedious prose what is already clear to the reader from a cursory examination of the tables and figures. If these have been well constructed, they will expose both the results and the experimental design (see Step 10). Little remains, then, but to make the object of each experiment clear in the text; to point out salient features, e.g., that A is greater than B (without giving the values), that something is linear over a certain range of concentration, or what the pH optimum is; and to connect the results with one another. In short, advise your students to *allow the data to speak for themselves* and to remember that the busy reader will be grateful for a guiding hand but should not be led as though blindfolded.

Authorities differ on whether the Results section should contain any conclusions. Some readers prefer to draw their own conclusions, without being prejudiced by the author, and compare them with the author's when they come to the Discussion section. If, however, the author keeps his Results section untainted by conclusions only to be forced to restate his findings in order to make the Discussion intelligible, he has avoided Scylla only to be drawn into Charybdis, for repetitiveness is a sin indeed. The best guide to offer is, perhaps, that the Results section must be comprehensible on its own and should indicate at least the *trend* of the author's reasoning, but that any extended discussion of the observations or comparison with others' work is best deferred until the last section. If no extended discussion is contemplated, the sections should be combined.

STEP 18: *Discussion Section*

This section is often the heart of a paper, the section in which the author assesses the meaning of his results. One can understand, then, why howls of protest go up when an editor suggests shortening it. However, the author should recognize that the minute consideration of every aspect of his work may not be as intensely interesting to others as it is to him, and there is a grave danger, if he indulges himself in a too-particular contemplation of nonessentials, that his reader may leave him before he has reached the nub of his argument. Again, he should realize that his natural desire to score off another investigator is only of marginal interest to the reader (unless he be that investigator) and, anyway, the pages of a journal are not the best place for personal rivalry. Try this as a piece of advice, then: *watch for symptoms of megalomania.*

Controversial issues should be discussed lucidly and fairly. Where results differ from previous ones, an explanation rather than a refutation should be sought. Anomalous results for which no explanation is readily available should be stressed rather than concealed, and the anomalies frankly admitted. Most interesting and valuable to science are the results which open up new possibilities of exploration, and these should be brought to the fore. Of course, *speculation* is in order in a Discussion, but it must be reasonable, firmly founded in observation, and subject to test, if it is to get past a responsible editorial board. A single hypothesis to explain results is almost mandatory, but piling hypothesis upon hypothesis is bad for the reader's digestion and the author's reputation. Sometimes the claim is made that some reader, somewhere, may be stimulated by the groping theories of an author, who should therefore not be forced to be too cut-and-dried. I think this notion is often grossly exaggerated. Only a very conceited man will seriously consider that science cannot advance unless his haphazard conjectures are enshrined in hallowed print.

5
The First Revision:
Structural Alterations

YOU WILL NEED:
Short versions of the "Condensation of Methods Section" assignment.

YOU SHOULD REREAD:
Trelease, pp. 44–46.

TIMING:
½–¾ hour.

ASSIGNMENT:
Steps 11, 12 of the student's journal article.

Revision of the first draft is best carried out in two distinct stages, described in Steps 19 and 20. In general, the less experienced the author, the more revisions are likely to be necessary; possibly, each of the following fractions of steps (subsumed under 19 and 20) may lead to a fresh draft. Teach your students not to be ashamed of four, five, or even more drafts—the greatest authors, whose prose looks as if it flowed effortlessly onto the page, have confessed to anywhere from 8 to 39 drafts before they were satisfied. Since perfection in the subtleties of literary style is not our aim, less revision than this should suffice, especially if it is logically directed and systematically undertaken.

STEP 19: *Are Major Alterations Necessary?*

Offer here four pieces of advice, given in the following order.

(a) SEEK OUT LOGICAL FLAWS

The ways in which a scientist can delude himself into believing that a cherished hypothesis has been proved are many and various. Trelease, pp. 44–46, trenchantly describes the most common ones. Of course, the purpose of all the hard thinking that went into the construction of the outlines was to avoid the possibility of any catastrophic failure of logic, so we shall expect the major argument to stand up without trouble. But there may be minor lines of reasoning that will not survive close scrutiny. Advise your students, therefore, to read those three pages of Trelease's book with the closest possible attention (the passage is so succinctly written that each sentence yields its full import only if one reads it two or three times and ponders it well). They should then consider every statement and inference in their first draft, sentence by sentence, for faults of logic. Few things give a better training in scientific method than the ruthless examination of one's own statements in the light of well-defined principles.

(b) CORRECT ANY MISQUOTATIONS

The writer should inspect with particular care his statements about others' work. Impress on your students that they must reread at this point the papers or passages of papers cited in the first draft and acquit themselves of any suspicion of misinterpretation—for an author's prejudices only too readily distort his remembrance of an earlier worker's conclusions. Students should guard even more carefully against the common tendency to cite a finding that has no true bearing on the point under discussion but merely relates to the same complex of ideas. Quoting out of context to give an impression different from that intended is, of course, universally condemned.

I doubt very much that the writer who commits these offenses does so in a deliberate attempt to deceive. The errors come from self-deception and wishful thinking, from a false recollection, or from notes that are too sketchy. Above all, the writer should recognize that his frame of reference has almost certainly changed since he first planned his research and read the articles cited. He owes it to his readers, and even more to himself, to read the articles again in the light of his present knowledge and attitudes and to assure himself that he is not quoting them incorrectly in either the letter or the spirit. For whatever the motives or reasons behind misquotation, the consequences are always unfortunate: knowledgeable readers (including editors and reviewers) lose confidence in the writer's competence, while the ignorant are misled.

To those who grumble that it is immense labor to read all that literature again, be merciless. Scholarship is not compatible with laziness, and science cannot progress where sloppy thinking is condoned. To put forward a hypothesis without checking the accuracy of the supporting arguments is like determining the composition of reaction products without being sure that the starting materials are pure.

You may wish to suggest this examination of the cited literature at an earlier stage—Step 11: Construct the Topic Outline. But I believe that this advice is valuable only to scientists with considerable experience in writing journal articles. Indeed, in planning the Introduction and Discussion, such writers should reexamine the leading sources of the arguments they will employ there. Novices, though, are all too easily distracted and discouraged from the task of writing their first drafts, and this rereading of published work may provide merely another tempting excuse for procrastination. If the reevaluation comes after the first draft has been written, the author has gained some confidence in his ability to write and is therefore willing to face the task of remodeling, should this seem called for.

(c) Reexamine the Order of Presentation

Even if no changes under (a) and (b) seem necessary, and even though Topic and Sentence Outlines were constructed and dutifully followed, make the student take a long, hard look at the first draft and consider whether it is soundly designed. He should ask himself in particular: "Will the function of each section be clear to any reader on his very first approach?"

Since clarity of purpose is the key to unity and coherence, the student should now refresh his memory about the exact intent of the article he is preparing, by reference to his title and synopsis. His main object at this stage is to ensure that the paths of reasoning in the first draft, rough and stony though they may be at present, at least point resolutely toward the goals he has defined.

If work on the Outlines has been thorough, shifting of material from one section to another should not, of course, be necessary. But miscalculations are always possible. The very process of writing the first draft may have revealed that a more logical development would result if facts and ideas were rearranged within the original framework. If so, now is the time for the scissors and paste—not later, for then the arduous dovetailing of each sentence to fit its context would have to be undertaken twice.

(d) COMBINE OR SIMPLIFY TABLES WHERE NECESSARY

A closer look at the tables drawn up in Step 10 may now reveal that portions of them are irrelevant to the point being made, or that two or more of them can be combined to increase comprehensibility. Similarly, graphs may profitably be reconstituted to convey their message more directly or vividly. Some principles that should underlie this revision are given in Chapter 10.

Step 19 has been largely concerned with logic and structure. When any major alterations necessitated by this step have been made, and not before, the student can proceed to the correction and improvement of style.

STEP 20: *Polishing the Style*

Style is probably what your students expected, in a course on writing, to hear about from the start. A few will have been disappointed not to have heard it mentioned, but most will have been relieved that you have been primarily concerned with something familiar and dear to them—scientific method. These need not feel they are entering foreign territory even now, if you emphasize that good scientific style consists of these qualities:

> rational construction of sentence and paragraph (*logic* again);
> absolute accuracy of expression (*precision*);
> ready comprehensibility (*clarity*);
> *directness*; and
> *brevity*.

Thus the scientific writer need strive only to be logical, precise, clear, direct, and brief. Most desiderata of literary style—for example, grace, mystery, urbanity, wit, lightness, word-music, rhythm—are, although not necessarily undesirable, inessential here. I think you will have little difficulty in persuading your students of the importance and desirability of good style *as thus defined*. For their greater comfort, stress that good scientific style can be learned: it is a craft rather than an art—by which I mean that it demands no special inspiration, or genius, that stamps a man as different from all others. Such inspiration, in a scientist, will have manifested itself at an earlier stage of the work: in the choice of problem, the experimental design, and the deductions. These you do not pretend to teach.

The discussion of scientific style (Chapter 6) will occupy at least three complete sessions, so it will constitute a considerable apparent digression from the numbered series of steps. You may like, therefore, to state at this time what the remaining steps will be (Chapter 8), in order to convey the feeling that completion of the task is somewhere in sight.

6

Further Revision:
Polishing the Style

The over-all plan for the sessions on style that constitute Step 20 is as follows.

First session: consideration of the true aims of style in scientific writing; enunciation of four principles of scientific style, with examples; assignment of sentences and phrases for correction.

Second session: consideration in class of answers to the assignments; discussion of points of special difficulty and any necessary amplification; discussion of the recommended reading list; and distribution of the "editing assignment"—a complete, badly written paper for correction (see Chapter 7).

Third session: correction of the "editing assignment" in class, preferably with the help of an overhead projector. After this, students should be able to proceed to apply the stylistic principles to the revision of their First Draft.

This schema should be flexible: four sessions may be needed.

YOU WILL NEED:

First Session
1. Copies of the book list, p. 56 (to be discussed in the Second Session; you will, however, refer to it in the first). This is a suggested *short* list to be handed out to your students; for full bibliography for your own reference, see the beginning of each chapter and the Bibliography of Further Reading, p. 179.
2. Copies of assignments related to each of the principles of style discussed (for suggested assignments see pp. 42, 48, 52, and 54).
3. Desk copies of (for full bibliographic details see p. 56): Fowler (*Modern English Usage*); Fowler and Fowler (*The King's English*); Gowers (*The Complete Plain Words*); Strunk and White (*The Elements of Style*); Quiller-Couch (*The Art of Writing*); Baker, J. R. 1955. "English Style in Scientific Papers." *Nature*. 176: 851–2.

Second Session
1. As above, plus copies of Baker's article for distribution.
2. Duplicated lists of the "Warning Words," see p. 51.
3. Copies of the Editing Assignment (see Chapter 7; have only the faulty text on the left-hand pages duplicated, with the superscript numbers omitted and with each line numbered for easy reference. See pp. 55 and 57 for preparation of alternative editing assignments).

Third Session
Transparent (Diops) copies of item 3 under Second Session.

You SHOULD READ:

All the books on the students' book list, p. 56.
The recommended passages on p. 42.
Fowler (*Modern English Usage*): entries headed "Unattached participles"; "Participles"; "Fused participles."
Author's Guide for Technical Reporting (Office of Scientific and Technical Information, Office of Aerospace Research, U.S. Air Force, July 1964, publication OAR 64-8, available from the U.S. Department of Commerce, Office of Technical Services, Washington, D.C. 20235).

STEP 20:   [*First Session*]

THE AIMS OF SCIENTIFIC STYLE

All that you have told your students up to now has laid a firm *foundation* for good scientific style, for it has been concerned with clear, logical thinking. Getting one's thoughts in good order is one of the hardest tasks in the world, especially if they are complex, novel, and exciting, and there will have been little chance during the preparation of the first draft to hunt and trap the telling word or to perfect the economical phrase. Now comes the time to polish the style.

Make it plain from the start that "style" is not an ornament applied to the outside of something essentially simple in order to dress it up for greater impressiveness. Stylistic improvement in scientific writing goes, generally, in quite the opposite direction. Explain that you will first bring to your students' notice some of the common faults of style in scientific literature, and then show how they can be avoided.

Define here what you mean by faults of style: impediments to the transfer of ideas. Ideally, sentences should be smooth; but if the price of smoothness is ambiguity, something clumsier but unequivocal is better. Brevity, we have said, is desirable; yet a long, precise statement is always preferable

to a concise one that is inexact. In other words, the students should aim not
at superficial graces but at functional beauty. To do so they must know
what the function of scientific prose is: to convey logically ordered ideas
exactly, concisely, and clearly.

There are many excellent books full of advice on how to achieve clarity
in writing (see the bibliography, pp. 179–184). You will do well to commend
Strunk's classic above all others. Strunk is concerned also, as are Gowers
and Quiller-Couch, with directness and vigor. These are indeed admirable
qualities in expository writing. But a goal that is rarely stressed in general
books on writing, one that is of particular importance in science and of
particular appeal to scientists (for obvious and good reasons), is precision.
You should not hesitate to stress this special quality in *scientific* writing,
both as a desideratum and as a strong suit in the scientist's hand.

However excellent the texts that you encourage your students to read
may be, the words of wisdom will not take root unless their meaning is
brought home by a great deal of practice. Numerous assignments that will
provide this practice are offered to you here. Elementary faults are dealt
with first, in single sentences or phrases, and more subtle and interesting
ones are presented later in the Editing Assignment (Chapter 7), in which
the student edits an entire article.

Obviously, the discussion of style must have a well-defined structure if
it is not to degenerate into the consideration of a multitude of single instances from which no precepts emerge. I suggest a framework of four stylistic principles to supply this structure. A detailed description of each of
them is given below. These principles have not been conceived in vacuo, but
have emerged from my own experience in editing scientific articles. They are
not infallible, and can and should be violated when there are overriding
reasons for doing so. For that reason they are best regarded as principles
rather than rules, although it is simpler and shorter to refer to Rule 1, Rule
2, and so on.

Make clear that you do not mean that the "rules" should impose some
restriction on the author's style from without; rather, good style grows
from within as the principles are first understood, then applied, and finally
transcended. The principles do not by any means supply the answer to
every stylistic problem, but if the student learns and understands them
thoroughly he will have acquired a writing technique that has a firm basis.
Most important of all, by studying and applying these principles the stu-

dents learn a *method* for criticizing their own writing. The method involves rational consideration of the purposes of writing, the application of well-defined principles, and the constant reappraisal of "rules" given here and elsewhere. What could be more congenial to a research scientist?

First, warn your students *not* to aim for the currently accepted style of scientific writing. They should *not* study the leading journal in their specialty and attempt to imitate the writing it contains. Unfortunately, there has grown up among scientists a ritualistic mode of expression that is at once grandiose and alien to science's grand purpose—which is surely explanation, not obfuscation. To combat this false style, arm your students for the fray with these firm intentions: to think straight, to say what they mean, and to ensure by constant consideration of their audience that what they say will be understood. Encourage them to treasure their native directness, and to spurn, not imitate, the tortured prose of others.

Fowler and Fowler begin their classic, *The King's English*, with this powerful sentence: "Any one who wishes to become a good writer should endeavour, before he allows himself to be tempted by the more showy qualities, to be direct, simple, brief, vigorous, and lucid." This admonition applies to all expository writing, but as we have seen, scientific writing demands one other quality: precision. The following enunciation and discussion of four principles of scientific style show, with examples, how Fowler and Fowler's five characteristics—and the additional characteristic, precision—can be attained in scientific writing. The resultant prose is, in functional beauty, as far beyond the tortured Gothic outpourings of current scientific writing as the buildings of Mies van der Rohe are beyond those of the Smithsonian.

Rule 1, *Be Simple and Concise*, works toward being "direct, simple, brief" and combats the tendency of the immature writer to be bombastic and verbose. Rule 2, *Make Sure of the Meaning of Every Word*, aims at precision; the rigorous application of this simple principle can not only increase accuracy of thought but also eradicate most of the grammatical faults common in scientific writing. Rule 3, *Use Verbs instead of Abstract Nouns*, enables your students to write more vigorously. Finally, their writing becomes both more precise and more lucid if they *Break Up Noun Clusters and Stacked Modifiers* (Rule 4), which creep so insidiously into the hasty or thoughtless writer's work. Let us see, then, how these rules can be imparted and how they work out in practice.

RULE 1: BE SIMPLE AND CONCISE

This most fundamental rule of expository writing can be introduced, if you will, by a delightful anecdote from Plutarch. It illustrates that from ancient times thoughtful men were aware of the danger of letting their tongues run away with them. "Anacharsis, when he had been feasted and entertained at Solon's house and lay down to sleep, was seen to have his left hand placed upon his private parts, but his right hand upon his mouth; for he believed, quite rightly, that the tongue needs the stronger restraint."

What was Anacharsis afraid of? That if he allowed himself to babble, some secret might be revealed. If a writer allows himself to babble in print, an even greater secret may come out: that he is not quite sure what he is talking about. He may have become so lost in impressive, orotund phrases that he is no longer able to face the issues squarely. One sure way to come to grips with a line of reasoning and examine whether it is logical is to express it in the simplest possible terms. For his own sake, then, as well as for the reader's, the writer should check through the first draft of his text—word by word and sentence by sentence—with these questions: "What can be shortened or simplified? What can be eliminated altogether?" The time and hard work it takes to substitute the simple expression for a long-winded circumlocution are well invested, for the more practice the writer gets in simplifying his expressions, the clearer and more forceful become his vocabulary and his thinking.

One of the worst faults of current scientific writing is a kind of hypnotic prolixity. The reader of a scientific article often gets the uneasy feeling that it describes a rite, in which the investigators Jones, Smith, and Robinson circle solemnly among the crucibles, ecstatically intoning

"Optimal reaction conditions are approximated when . . .";

"In studies pertaining to the identification of phenolic derivatives, drying of the paper gives less satisfactory visualization";

and

"Insufficient data are at present available to completely negate the possibility that removal of the abovementioned substances from the circulation is not a factor of importance."

These are (real, not invented!) examples of *jargon*, the kind of magniloquent utterance that the specialist falls into when he forgets to strive for simplicity. The etymology of "jargon" is revealing: it is derived from a medieval French word meaning the warbling, twittering, and chattering of birds, and has the same root as "gargle." Jargon consists, then, of sounds that are meaningless. It often results when words are borrowed from one scholarly vocabulary, where they have a precise meaning, and used, in another discipline, in a pseudo-scholarly way. Thus "to approximate" has a precise meaning in mathematics, but the first of the above examples ("Optimal conditions are approximated when . . .") does not use this meaning (of continuous approach to an ideal, or ultimate value)*; the ornamental flourish actually says no more than "The reaction goes fastest when. . ." (Or does the phrase mean "The reaction goes most nearly to completion when. . ."? Simple language enforces accurate *thinking*.) Thus, the writer is not merely verbose; he is inaccurate.

Impress upon your students with all the vigor at your command how dangerous an inflated style is, not merely in obscuring meaning for the reader but in so veiling the issue from the *writer* that the chances of his making a blunder are greatly increased.

The second ritualistic example,

"In studies pertaining to the identification of phenolic derivatives, drying of the paper gives less satisfactory visualization,"

may seem innocuous to those of your students whose sensibilities have already become calloused by daily contact with scientific writing at its present low standard. Ask them if they don't prefer

"Phenolic derivatives are more easily seen and identified if the paper is left wet."

Some may be so far corrupted as to be shocked by the "bluntness" of the restatement. Others will admit that they prefer it, but object that it may not be what the author meant. This objection brings out a prime justification for simplifying high-flown passages: they are usually ambiguous. Still others may feel that although the simpler form communicates more easily and vividly, the difference is slight. Get these objectors to realize that a writer who permits himself one such pompous sentence will almost certainly persist in his stylelessness, constantly being complex where he could be simple. Each small, unnecessary effort of comprehension the reader must

---

* Writers have become so careless in thinking about the meaning of words that I have recently seen "The amount of X was approximated by . . ." when the writer meant "estimated" or "determined"!

make tires and frets him, and lessens his receptiveness even if he escapes being consciously bored.

You can draw here an analogy between the writer and an archer who points his bow at a target (the reader's comprehension) a hundred yards away. It is the archer's responsibility to trim his arrows and take his aim, not the target's to swell so that it can be hit. An error of a centimeter at the firing end means a yard off the bull's eye. The real danger is that complacency about such poor aim, such small lapses into unnecessary complexity, quickly leads to monstrosities like the "insufficient data" sentence above or to:

"A variety of stimulatory hormones, irrespective of their chemical nature, are characterized by their ability to influence the synthesis of messenger RNA as a prerequisite for the secondary biologic events characteristic of the particular target organ."

Have your students rewrite this sentence in simple prose, and discover for themselves how little they understand it, how wide of the mark its author was.

At this point, you may have to counter students' protestations that you seem to be opposed to the use of technical terms. Naturally, you are not. Technical terms are often polysyllabic, yet they are concise because they have precise (if often complex) meanings that would require many more words to convey in any other way. But in habituating ourselves to these polysyllabic terms we become inclined to use other polysyllabic words and phrases that sound dignified but that turn out on examination to be merely pretentious. In the bad sentence above, the only technical term is "messenger RNA"—and this is the clearest feature of the whole sentence! Give your class a common example of fuzziness induced by nontechnical verbiage: "under conditions of high pH." This says no more than "when the pH is high." Why bury pH, which says so much so succinctly, under the woolly blanket-word "conditions"? Encourage your students to develop and use a "thinking man's vocabulary," not the jargon of the pseudo-intellectual. "A man of true science uses but few hard words, and those only when none other will answer his purpose; whereas the smatterer in science thinks that by mouthing hard words he proves that he understands hard things." (Herman Melville)

You may also have to counter another kind of objection. Certain fields engender a special terminology, which, the students say, is perfectly well understood and indeed is a useful shorthand way of conveying information within the charmed circle of its most active practitioners. They admit that it may be misunderstood by outsiders, but suspect that they may not become accepted members of the "in-group" if they fail to follow the leaders' example. Calm their fears on this score. Even "club members" are susceptible to the appeal of clear, simple English and will never even notice when jargon is missing. Ask your students if they want to reach *only* the members of the in-group. Are they bent on repelling others? Do they want their papers to have lasting value, or are they content to see them become quickly outmoded because of the perishable cargo of vogue words they bear? Discourage them, too, from the propagation of neologisms. A little thought, and a little dictionary work, will often produce an exactly equivalent, already existing, English word to substitute for their uncalled-for brain-child.

I have, in contrast to the authors of many books on style, put simplicity and conciseness together under one heading, for I believe they should be aimed at *simultaneously*. Otherwise a whole group of students will produce, in a laudable attempt only to be simple, this kind of verbose passage:

"The numbers of enucleated cells in vaccinated and nonvaccinated mice were determined both at four and eight days after inoculation and (or) the beginning of fasting. The number of enucleated cells in vaccinated mice was seen to be greater than in nonvaccinated mice and to increase from four to eight days after inoculation, whereas the number of such cells examined under the same conditions in nonvaccinated mice actually decreased during the first part of the experimental period and then increased from four to eight days, but not to the same extent as they did in mice that were both vaccinated and fasted. Consideration of the numbers of enucleated cells in all four groups, see Table 1, reveals that the effect of fasting seems to have been superimposed upon the effect of prior vaccination, at least in the second portion of the experimental period."

As Strunk puts it, "conciseness requires not that the writer make all his sentences short, or that he avoid all detail and treat his subjects only in outline, but that *every word tell*" (his Rule 13, p. 17). Few words tell in this "simple" passage, which is therefore as tedious to read as if it had been wrapped up in polysyllabic elaborations.

Further invaluable reading on what constitutes nontechnical jargon is to be found in the following (for complete references see p. 56):

1. Gowers, *The Complete Plain Words*. Recommend that your students read at least *case* (pp. 91–2), *position, situation, conditions*, and *level* (pp. 138–141). The last-named has acquired enormous popularity with the development of molecular genetics (use of such phrases as *at the transcription level* has led to absurd imitations like *at the membrane level*, where *level* is completely superfluous). Ask them what they would think if you told them that you are dealing with writing *at the ideational level*.
2. Strunk, Rules 12 (p. 15) and 13 (p. 17).
3. Quiller-Couch, Chapter V, "On jargon." This classic deserves to be learned by heart.
4. Baker's two-page paper, see beginning of this chapter.

Show your students, by requiring them to read these short excerpts, how entertaining books on style can be. It is not sufficient to place the books on a "recommended reading" list—you must whet the students' appetite for them.

A list of complicated sentences for simplification and condensation is given below. Indubitably you can supplement this list from your current reading.

EXERCISES ON RULE 1 (with suggested corrections)
This phenomenon is associated, in a causative or accompanying way, with . . .
    (This phenomenon causes or accompanies)
At the termination of the experiment . . .
    (At the end of the experiment)
. . . has the capability of . . .
    (can, is able to)
. . . at a high speed level . . .
    (quickly, rapidly)
This result would seem to indicate the possible presence of . . .
    (This result indicates that . . . may be present.)
Effectiveness of the oral inoculum in producing caries varies widely with the strain of rat; in some cases, rats may become highly caries active, whereas in other strains, the oral inoculum has much less adverse influence.
    (delete everything after the semicolon)
X produced an inhibitory effect on the formation of Y.
    (X inhibited the formation of Y.)
It was possible to obtain semipreparative (100 μg) quantities of substance X.
    (About 100 μg of X could be made.)
X formed Y at least an order of magnitude faster when . . .
    (X formed Y at least ten times faster when)

Computations were conducted . . .

    (Calculations were made; or, X was calculated)

. . . in a state of protrusion . . .

    (protruding)

. . . subsequent to their entry into the cell . . .

    (after they have entered the cell)

. . . occupies a juxta-nuclear position . . .

    (is next to the nucleus)

Solvents were pre-cooled at 0°C prior to use.

    (What does "pre-cooled" have over "cooled," or "prior to" over "before"?)

One lot contained particles greater than 74 μ, and this material was shaken on a sieve prior to use to remove particles in excess of this size.

    (One lot contained particles *larger* than 74 μ; these were removed by sieving.)

Figs. 1–3 are photographs of thin-layer chromatograms developed in the solvent system described and are typical of the separations achieved with this chromatographic method.

    (Figs. 1–3 show typical chromatograms.)

Rule 2: Make Sure of the Meaning of Every Word

"Alice had not the slightest idea what Latitude was, or Longitude either, but she thought they were nice grand words to say."

Science is full of nice grand words, and very tempting to tongue and pen they are. But if a major objective of our writing, as of all our scientific activity, is precision, we must use them with the greatest care. If we try to write without understanding their meaning *exactly*, it is like trying to obtain a result with uncalibrated equipment, while revision is like trying to find a fault in the equipment without understanding the basic principles of its construction. Insist, then, that your students calibrate their equipment by frequent recourse to dictionaries (for words of general meaning) and to textbooks (for definitions of technical terms).

Be patient with your students. They entered quite suddenly, at college, a world of ideas peopled with a vast number of new words, some of which were never adequately explained, many of which are inaccurately used in the articles they read. The only adequate corrective is constant vigilance and a conscious appraisal of each word that they write. Ask them to consider (as examples of precision in word usage) whether enzyme reactions are studied in solutions of *varying enzyme concentration* or in solutions of *various enzyme concentrations*. Is a *variety of improvements* reported, or are *various improvements* described? Did the clinician administer *varied* treatments or merely *different* ones? Are two values *equivalent* or *equal*? What is wrong with "Both methods yielded similar results," or with "The adsorption is completed in 15 minutes. This greatly reduces previously reported adsorption times."?

Your students may not be as patient with you as you are with them. "Oh, for pity's sake," they cry, "we know just what the fellow means, why all the pedantic fuss?" Convince them that this apparently robust, commonsense attitude is, in fact, a nonscientific one, analogous to that of a housewife who cannot conceive that an ounce of butter one way or the other is going to make the slightest difference in her cooking, whereas the scientist frequently encounters the case in which a milligram and even a microgram makes all the difference in the world. Anyway, *is* the reader so sure what "the fellow means"? If the writer's prose abounds in minor inaccuracies like this, we *cannot* be confident that when he refers to "10 mM glucose ... in a total of 3 ml" he actually used 3 ml of a 10 millimolar solution. The carelessness of his style makes it distressingly likely that he made a common error of abbreviation and actually meant "10 millimoles of glucose per 3 ml of solution." The 300-fold difference might well be crucial in an experiment.

For precision of diction, a knowledge of definitions is (of course) not enough. Besides the meanings of individual words, the writer must examine words *in context* to ensure that the correct meaning is conveyed. An intelligent university student without any formal knowledge of grammar can actually correct most faults in grammar simply by analyzing his sentences logically. Can anyone fail to spot the error in "This value was found by Smith in rabbits who reported that . . . ," provided he is examining the meaning of every word and its context? Nevertheless, an awareness of common pitfalls is helpful. One such pitfall is the unattached or dangling participle; another, the dangling infinitive; a third, the omission of auxiliary verbs. A brief discussion of these points is worthwhile (although you may feel that continuity is best preserved if you defer this to the *second* style session). A treatment such as the following is suitable.

Dangling participles. Scientific writing abounds in dangling participles because it is difficult to combine successfully the frequently used (and useful) passive voice with a participial construction. As you know, a verb-form (participle or infinitive) is said to "dangle" when the (unstated) subject of the verb in question is *not* the subject of the main clause of the sentence.

A dangling participial construction may be unobjectionable ("The experiment was performed using redistilled solvents"), misleading ("Chromatography fractions were sampled, followed by UV measurement, and dried."), or downright ludicrous: "After closing the incision, the animal was placed in a restraining cage" (skillful surgeons, some of these laboratory animals!). Baker, in the article in *Nature* cited at the head of this chapter, states that "anyone who is intelligent enough to carry out scientific research at a university can easily grasp everything that it is essential to know about the use of present participles and gerunds in fifteen minutes." Although Dr. Baker may be optimistic, do give your students fifteen minutes of instruction on the point. As source material use Fowler on *Unattached participles*, the excellent example given by Baker, and horrid examples you have collected yourself. Recommend these simple precepts to be applied in revision of the first draft:

(a) In each sentence, establish the subject of every verb (in whatever form the verb may appear—active or passive voice, participle, infinitive). Ensure that the subject, if present, is unequivocally in the right context or, if absent or represented by a pronoun, is unambiguously implied.

(b) Distrust all words that end in ". . . ing" and examine their context for correctness (see Fowler on *Participles*, esp. *Fused participles*). Particularly avoid *following*, which is usually a clumsy elaboration for *after* but which sounds distressingly like a participle, to the confusion of all ("The milkiness of the intestinal lymphatics of a *dog following a fat meal. . .* ". Poor, starved animal! "Following the meeting in Paris, the editors visited London." How vague about a rendezvous can you get?)

Dangling infinitives. These are almost as common as dangling participles. Take, for example, the sentence "The flask was flushed with nitrogen to remove ozone." The intended subject of the verb "remove" is "the experimenter," but this subject is not mentioned. *Grammatically*, therefore, the implied subject of that verb must be the subject of the main clause—"flask"—and the nonsensical inference to be drawn is that the flask wanted to remove its excess ozone. The fault is *not* corrected by inserting "in order," since these words merely elucidate that the infinitive is an infinitive of purpose and do not essentially change the grammatical structure. Nor is the fault corrected by inverting the sentence to "Excess ozone was removed by flushing the flask with nitrogen," for then we have a dangling *participle*, "flushing" (grammatically, the ozone must be doing the flushing).

The best correction in most instances of this kind is to insert the true subject of all the verbs, namely "we," and transform the sentence into the active voice. "We flushed the flask with nitrogen (in order) to remove excess ozone" or "We removed excess ozone by flushing the flask with nitrogen." If the passive is considered essential, the possibilities (cumbersome but correct) are: "The flask was flushed with nitrogen and the excess ozone thereby removed"; "Flushing the flask with nitrogen removed excess ozone" (here the notion of *purpose* is not expressed, but is rather obvious; "flushing" in *this* sentence is not a participle but a gerund or verb-noun); and "In order that excess ozone might be removed, the flask was flushed with nitrogen."

Omitted auxiliaries. Avoidance of the repetition of "was" or "were" in a sentence—a device applied by many writers, perhaps in an unconscious attempt to decrease wordiness—requires careful handling if the sentence is to emerge grammatically correct. The following classification of omitted auxiliaries is readily understood and applied:

(a) *Invariably incorrect.* Two different verbs and two different subjects, one of which is singular and the other plural, e.g., "The rats were killed and their blood pooled." (Blood were pooled??)

(b) *Sometimes correct, rarely advisable.* Two (or more) verbs, each with its own subject, all subjects being singular (or all being plural): "The dog was anesthetized, blood drawn through a long needle provided with anticoagulant, and serum separated by centrifuging." Although grammatically correct, this kind of sentence plunges the reader into a succession of uncertainties. Are we supposed to read "blood drawn through a long needle was provided with anticoagulant" or "blood was drawn through a long needle [that had been] provided with anticoagulant"? Did the serum separate or was it separated? Insertion of "was" at two points would remove all doubts.

(c) *Always correct and desirable.* One subject, and a string of verbs, e.g., "The solution was warmed, stirred, decanted, and evaporated."

The writer (and reviser) can guard against errors that result from omitting auxiliaries if he again follows the advice (see above): establish the subject of each verb and ensure that its context is correct.

In general, it is not appropriate to deal with any other points of grammar in a course of this sort. Individual students who need grammatical help or study can be directed to such textbooks and workbooks as those by J. M. Walsh and A. K. Walsh, Archibald C. Jordan, or W. Paul Jones (see the bibliography, p. 179). Jones, Chapter 19, provides particularly appropriate examples and exercises on parallel construction, agreement of subject and verb, reference of pronouns, dangling, trailing, and misplaced modifiers, and other grammatical problems. Tichy (see students' book list, p. 56) deals with the matter of grammar sensibly, by reviewing only the kinds of mistake that are common in *scientists'* writing. It may amuse you to discover what a large proportion of the faults she lists can be detected by a conscientious reviser who applies Rule 2—to take two common examples, the unidentified or ambiguous antecedent of pronouns (detected by "what is the meaning of *it* or *this* here?") and the nonagreement of subject and verb (detected by "what is the meaning of the context of this verb, i.e., what is its subject?"). Your whole approach should be, I think, to get your students to rely on logical analysis for the removal of blemishes, rather than to give a full review of formal grammar.

Detailed analysis for meaning will often turn up scientific solecisms such as the following:

"The solvents were evaporated in vacuo at 40°C under a stream of nitrogen."

Here the author has been too lazy to examine the meaning of the words "in vacuo" that are daily on his lips—shouldn't this phrase be banished forever in favor of "at reduced pressure" if there is any danger of its leading to the absurdity of specifying that a vacuum shall be composed of nitrogen? Unmasking blunders such as this constitutes, surely, the whole justification for detailed criticism of one's writing.

Urge your students, then, to combine common sense with their not-so-common intelligence and to acquire an ingrained habit of ruthless word-by-word criticism. The ultimate object will be to make every sentence (as Quintilian put it) not merely capable of being understood, but incapable of being misunderstood. No writer, least of all a scientist, should lay himself open to the kind of reprimand that Alice received:

"Speak English!" said the Eaglet. "I don't know the meaning of half those long words, and, what's more, I don't believe you do either."

EXERCISES ON RULE 2

Ferric chloride was deleted from the color reagent.

(simple malapropism of "deleted" for "eliminated" or "omitted")

Glyceryl ethers of varying degrees of unsaturation . . .

(The continuous "varying" is inappropriately used instead of "various.")

A method is described for use on unfractionated human plasma that is superior to that now in use.

(Is the *plasma* superior to that now in use?)

The composition of the lymph of the fasted rat is also unlike depot fat.

(Is the composition unlike *fat*? This is a very common type of fault, eliminated by inserting "that of" before "depot fat.")

The addition of hexokinase decreased palmitate oxidation and was therefore not included in the incubation medium.

(The *addition* was not included?)

The optimal conditions for transesterification approximate those for phospholipase activity.

(not "approximate," which means "approach," but "are about the same as")

The two major components analyzed very close to that expected for the mono- and diacetate structures.

(1. Did the components analyze, or were they analyzed? 2. What is antecedent of "that"? 3. What is the use of the word "structures"?)

The problem of diffusion constants of almost insoluble substances . . .

(Are diffusion constants a problem?)

Due to the low resistance of the plate, a 100-ohm resistance was placed in series with it.

("Due to" is often advantageously replaced by "because of." Try inverting the sentence: it makes sense with "because of" but not with "due to.")

Following the incubation, the remaining fluid was poured off and the slices washed.

(1. Was the fluid following the incubation? Use "after." 2. The auxiliary verb "were" is omitted.)

The tubes were shaken, followed by centrifugation, and the upper phase withdrawn.

(Were the tubes followed by centrifugation? Were the upper phase withdrawn?)

Fasting blood was drawn.

(Can blood fast?)

In view of the colored nature of retinol . . .

(What is a colored nature? Can it come into view, as a color can?)

Based on electrophoretic patterns, hyperlipoproteinemias have been classified.

(Were hyperlipoproteinemias based on electrophoretic patterns?)

Other investigators have reported large populations of lactobacilli in fecal contents. Reference 7 presents a recent review dealing with this problem.

(Are large populations—at least in this context—a problem?)

In the steady state, the daily fecal excretion of neutral plus acidic steroids of endogenous origin should approximate the daily synthesis of cholesterol.

(. . . should approximately equal . . .)

Contrast this correct usage:

When radioactive cholesterol is given to patients with every meal, the specific activity of biliary bile acids approximates that of plasma cholesterol after some days.

and point out the strength and utility of precise vocabulary and usage.

RULE 3: USE VERBS INSTEAD OF ABSTRACT NOUNS

So far we have talked about being simple, brief, logical, and precise. Writing that has these characteristics can still be unappealing: noble and virtuous, perhaps, but lifeless. The Fowler brothers knew what they were about when they commended vigor as a prime characteristic of good writing. Lucas, too, remarks that it is not much use making your reader see, if you also make him yawn.

What is it that makes most scientific writing so preeminently dull? I believe it is the failure to use expressive verbs, for the best way to bring a piece of flabby writing to life is to use richly meaningful, telling verbs. Yet scientists seem to want to weaken the verb in every possible way. They show an inexplicable urge to use gerunds, abstract nouns derived from verbs, or noun-phrases—anything *but* a verb, in fact—to do the work in a sentence, which then has to be grammatically completed (since a sentence, by definition, demands a verb) by some pale shadow of a verb like "effected." Thus, instead of the vigorous "A was separated from B" we have to suffer "The separation of A from B was effected." The force of the verb "separate" has been dissipated by its transmutation into "separation." Your first task is, then, to train your students to recognize and then *release the hidden verb,* that sleeping beauty so often locked up in a bland ivory tower of an abstract noun.

Mention of the abstract noun brings up a second aspect of this principle of using verbs: it enables the writer to substitute concrete action for hazy abstractions, which, as every professional writer from antiquity to the present knows, is vital to holding your readers' interest. In scientific writing we are often dealing with, and necessarily writing about, abstract concepts.

All the more reason, then, to write concretely when no abstract idea is being put forward.

> "Isolation of the tertiary component was accomplished and its identifi-
> cation achieved by the following sequence of manipulations."

Here the scientist is not thinking, like some yearning recluse, of the accomplishment of isolation; he is thinking, and should be writing, about isolating a particular compound. Nor is he concerned, like a spiritual guru, with the ultimate achievement of identification; he just wants to identify a single chemical. When actions are earthbound, their description should be earthy —and vigorous.

The technique of releasing the hidden verb leads, as your best students will already have realized, not only to greater vigor but also to simplicity and brevity. Circumlocution is often the result of burying verbs in other, longer parts of speech (not "explain" but "is explanatory of"; not "results from" but "is the resultant of"). In addition, using verbs instead of nouns can lead to greater precision, because the proper use of a verb forces the writer to specify subject and object unequivocally. Abstract nouns allow the subject to remain unnamed and insubstantial, which is why the writer of official documents loves them so (see Gowers). In one example I encountered, I was able to conclude only after diligent search of the context that the sentence "Repeat aspiration was necessitated" probably meant "The upper layer had to be siphoned off twice"; I remained uncertain, however, since the subject "the upper layer" had not been specified.

Your advice will be, then, to release hidden verbs wherever feasible; but you will find that your students need much practice before they can recognize nouns (and other parts of speech) derived from verbs. A useful aid in doing so is to compile and keep at hand a list of "warning words" which usually indicate a nearby trapped verb in distress. These warning words are the colorless shadows of verbs I mentioned above as being necessary to complete the sentence in which an abstract verb-noun lurks: "carried out," "effected," "achieved," "facilitated," and the like. A list of them appears in Table 1. I suggest distributing this list in the Second Session, but you may prefer to do so here. Do not call them "forbidden words," because in some contexts they are inevitable and right. But they should be memorized as warning signals. When the student finds one of them as he revises his first draft, he should stop at once and examine the sentence closely. Can it be expressed more succinctly, precisely, directly, vigorously? Almost always he will discover that it can.

TABLE 1 *"Warning Words"*

These are to be regarded not as invariably undesirable words, but as warning signals that something may be amiss, or susceptible of improvement. One soon gets into the habit of noticing them at a glance, on any page.

Colorless verbs (usually to be eliminated; they occur most commonly as the past participle, as shown)

accomplished	experienced	obtained
achieved	facilitated	occurred
attained	given	performed
carried out	implemented	proceeded
conducted	indicated	produced
done	involved	required
effected	made	

Woolly words (sometimes these have a precise meaning; more often, they are an indication that the thought has to be sharpened)

area	problem
character	process
conditions	situation
field	structure
level	system
nature	

Words incorrectly used as synonyms

amount	alternate	minimal	varying
concentration	alternative	negligible	various
content		slight	varied
level			different

Dangling words
All words that end in "ing" or "ed" and all infinitives

Danger words

this (obscure antecedent)	their, its, and all
it (obscure antecedent)	other pronouns

Vague qualifiers (can usually be omitted, since they add nothing)

fairly   quite   rather   several   very   much

EXERCISES ON RULE 3

Protein determinations were performed as described above.

(Proteins were determined as described above.)

Hydriodic acid attack on unsaturated ethers proceeds at olefinic bonds.

(Hydriodic acid attacks unsaturated ethers at olefinic bonds.)

Conversion of acetates to iodides was effected.

(Acetates were converted to iodides.)

Primary and secondary particle separation was obtained by performing electro-phoresis.

(Primary and secondary particles were separated by electrophoresis. "Per-forming" is both dangling and redundant.)

Injection of the protein was more difficult of achievement in older animals due to the frequency of occurrence of thrombosis.

(It was more difficult to inject the protein into older animals because thrombi often formed.)

Preferential release of monoenoic acids would also appear to be the case in man.

(Monoenoic acids seem to be preferentially released in man also.)

The separations were checked frequently to ensure that quantitative recovery of cholesteryl esters, uncontaminated by triglycerides, was being achieved in the second fraction.

(Frequent checks established that cholesteryl esters, uncontaminated by triglycerides, were recovered quantitatively in the second fraction.)

The paper lost its integrity.

(The paper disintegrated.)

There was predominantly protein formation . . .

(Proteins were mostly formed . . .)

RULE 4: BREAK UP NOUN CLUSTERS AND STACKED MODIFIERS

A factor that contributes significantly to the flexibility of English is that one noun can be used to modify another without any inflection. Thus, "disease of the liver" can be perfectly satisfactorily rendered as "liver disease" even though an adjectival form for liver, "hepatic," exists. When more than two nouns are gathered together, however, trouble begins. In "adult liver disease" we become uncertain which words are substantive and which modi-fying: is the writer referring to liver disease in the adult, or to disease of the adult liver? Here, perhaps, it does not greatly matter; the phrase makes sense whichever way you group the words, just as in "rabbit ear skin" or "serum cholesterol level." But when we encounter "liver disease plasma" the case is different. Does this mean "disease(d) plasma flowing through the liver," "hepatic plasma in disease"? No, the only meaningful combina-tion seems to link the two first nouns to form a complex adjective and make the phrase mean "plasma obtained from patients with liver disease."

The meaning of these noun clusters can, then, usually be puzzled out—although sometimes a real, unresolvable ambiguity results, as in "heavy beef heart mitochondria protein" (which is heavy—the beef, the heart, the mitochondria, or the protein?). The major objection to noun clusters is that the writer has shown discourtesy in using a shorthand designation that may be convenient for him but is highly inconvenient for the reader.

The difficulty is compounded when not only a couple of nouns, but a whole string of modifiers, is cavalierly flung down before a single noun. Here real uncertainty arises as to what is meant to modify what. Except to an expert in the field, the meaning of "a radium containing argon ionization chamber" is totally obscure. Perhaps you think that a little reflection will unscramble this: the chamber, which contains radium, is a device for ionizing argon—why bother to add words spelling it out? My answer is twofold. First, the onus of making the translation should not be on the reader. Second, the translation is *wrong*: the chamber does contain both argon and radium, but the "ionization" is of organic vapors that enter the chamber and react with the electrically excited argon. So much for the attitude "Oh, they'll all know what I mean!"

If the reader is in as much of a hurry as the writer of such careless phrases, understanding may never be reached. In a paper in which a reader has become used to translating "silica gel coated glass fiber paper chromatography" into "chromatography on paper that is made out of glass fibers and coated with silica gel," "nonglucose light experiments" into "experiments carried out in the light in the absence of glucose," and "light glucose cells" into (believe it or not) "cells grown in the light in the presence of glucose," he will almost certainly be waiting for the main verb in "The presence of glucose delayed daughter cell release in 80% of experiments . . . ," only to discover after much cogitation that the main verb is actually there! The noun cluster consists of only three words, *daughter cell release*, and the sentence is meant to be read: "The presence of glucose delayed the release of daughter cells in 80% of experiments." Readers with this degree of perseverance are more than such an author deserves.

How should one detect clusters of nouns and modifiers, judge whether they impede communication, and correct them if they do? Detection is easy, if tedious. The student should pick out every noun in his draft and count the number of modifiers it bears. A useful rule of thumb to ensure lucidity is to allow the coupling of two nouns ("palmitate oxidation") but not the addition of a third ("sheep palmitate oxidation") nor even of a modifier of the two-noun cluster ("enhanced palmitate oxidation"). And the correction is also rather simple: decide the precise relationship of the modifiers to one another, and express this relationship by inserting prepositions and verbs. Some loss of brevity is inevitable, but lucidity is too important a commodity to be sacrificed on the altar of conciseness, and you should not allow your students to defend their clusters with Rule 1 as their banner. This is one example, out of many you will encounter, of the need to overrule one principle because of the greater importance of another.

Exercises on Rule 4

The monoamine oxidase inhibitor insensitive agent
   (The agent that is insensitive to the inhibitor of monoamine oxidase)
Radioactive glycerol-labeled triglyceride metabolism
   (Metabolism of triglycerides labeled with radioactive glycerol)
Anomalous stability constant order
   (Anomalous order of stability constants)
. . . in order to obtain high purity, high yield aldehyde
   (. . . in order to obtain aldehyde in high purity and high yield)
Highly purified heavy beef heart mitochondria protein
   (Protein from the highly purified heavy fraction of bovine heart mitochondria)
Proteolipid protein-free lower phase lipids
   (Lipids contained in the lower phase, free from proteolipid protein)
Cellulose acetate electrophoresis procedure
   (Electrophoresis on cellulose acetate)

The minute analysis of imperfect prose that is necessary to illustrate principles such as the ones I have given may seem irksome. Elaboration of these points is indeed unnecessary to a naturally gifted writer, who instinctively avoids the kind of solecism I have discussed. But it is to the less gifted that our attention is directed, to the student who senses that something is wrong, but who does not know why, or how corrections can be made. He needs clearcut principles—principles he can see the point of, and believe in—to guide his hand and brain. If you can demonstrate that by application of these simple principles a passage is markedly improved, the student rapidly discovers that the process is exciting rather than tedious, and develops a style that is a worthy vehicle for the liveliness of his thought.

STEP 20: *[Second Session]*

After the students have wrestled with the short assignments, it is advisable to discuss the four principles again, with the aid of further examples, in order that the students not only grasp them but become thoroughly familiar with them. You can distribute the "Warning Words" (Table 1) as a basis for this amplification. The first part of the table lists colorless verbs and is to be related to Rule 3; the rest of the table refers to various aspects of Rule 2.

The grammatical points I discussed under Rule 2 (dangling constructions and omitted auxiliary verbs) can also now be considered.

Discuss the short book list (p. 56), distinguish between books to be read thoroughly and those to be used for reference, and ensure that the students have embarked on some reading of them. The "highly recommended" books can be described with enthusiasm to those of your students who have some literary bent and appreciation and who have already mastered the Four Rules, but do not launch into this encomium too early; the student must tangle with and overcome the fundamental difficulties before he can appreciate these elegant and eloquent pleas for better style. Even the lively book by Tichy, which is specifically directed toward scientists, should be regarded as the basis of *further* refinement of style rather than as an introductory text. One great strength of this appealing book is the wealth of examples in which scientist-writers have succeeded, in contrast to the many I have quoted who have failed, in the task of scientific communication.

Distribute the Editing Assignment (examples are provided in Chapter 7) and explain to your students that it is so loaded with faults that they will certainly have to rewrite every sentence, at least in part, and reorganize some of the paper as well. In particular, they should examine the Table for possible simplification, and consider whether any material should be moved from the Results to the Methods section or vice versa. Tell them that you will go over this paper in detail in the next session, but that they should correct it, as far as they are able, before then. Emphasize that they should read the faulty article right through before giving way to the natural urge to start correcting: only if the point of the article is understood will the editing be soundly based.

"Editing assignments" such as the examples I have given can be com-

BOOKS ON (SCIENTIFIC) WRITING

Essential textbooks:

Strunk, W., Jr. 1959. *The Elements of Style*. Macmillan Co., New York and London (paperback 1962). Original form copyrighted 1918.

Trelease, S. F. 1958. *How to Write Scientific and Technical Papers*. Williams and Wilkins, Baltimore, Md. (Paperback: The M.I.T. Press, Cambridge, Mass., 1969.) Earlier versions, by the same author under similar titles, are not as good. Page numbers in Trelease referred to in this manual are those in the 1958 hard-cover edition.

Reference works:

A good collegiate dictionary. Webster's is the most often referred to but is the most permissive; Random House is a better authority for educated usage. British writers will prefer the Oxford Dictionary.

Fowler, H. W. 1965. *A Dictionary of Modern English Usage*. 2nd edition. Oxford University Press, Oxford and New York. (First published 1926.)

Partridge, E. 1963. *Usage and Abusage*. Penguin Books, Harmondsworth, Middlesex and Baltimore, Md. (First published 1947.)

Roget's Thesaurus. Innumerable versions, including paperback editions. (First published 1852.)

Conference of Biological Editors, Committee on Form and Style. 1964. *Style Manual for Biological Journals*. 2nd edition. American Institute of Biological Sciences, Washington, D.C.

Highly recommended:

Gowers, Sir Ernest. 1954. *The Complete Plain Words*. (Paperback: Penguin Books, Harmondsworth and Baltimore, 1963.)

Lucas, F. L. 1955. *Style*. Cassell, London. (Collier, New York, 1962; Pan, London, 1964.)

Quiller-Couch, Sir Arthur. 1916. *The Art of Writing*. (Paperback: Capricorn Books, New York, 1961.)

Tichy, H. J. 1967. *Effective Writing for Engineers, Managers, Scientists*. John Wiley and Sons, New York and London.

Recommended:

Gensler, W. J., and K. D. Gensler. 1961. *Writing Guide for Chemists*. McGraw-Hill, New York and London (paperback).

Kane, T. S., and L. J. Peters. 1964. *Writing Prose: Techniques and Purposes*. 2nd edition. Oxford University Press, New York.

posed very easily. You may want to prepare one whose subject-matter has closer appeal for your particular class. Just take any *short*, well-written, published paper—one of your own, for instance—and inject into it examples of all the faults that have been discussed in the preceding pages plus others that you find especially objectionable. This can be done rapidly if you have before you a list of "Warning Words"; the exercises on the Four Rules; and compilations of circumlocutions, passive constructions, malapropisms, and clichés such as are contained in the tables, pp. 17–20, of the *Author's Guide for Technical Reporting* (see bibliography at the beginning of this chapter). Everything in this excellent booklet is worth studying, for possible use with your students later.

STEP 20: [*Third Session*]

YOU WILL NEED:

A copy of the "editing assignment" distributed at the end of the Second Session, identical with the students' copies except that it is made on transparent Diops (sheets of clear plastic); a supply of sharpened wax pencils; and an overhead projector that throws onto a screen an image of the sheet and of your pencil as you make corrections.

If you do not have the facilities to have such Diops made, use an ordinary copy of the assignment and a projector such as is used for projecting an image of a page in a book. You will not be able to make corrections on the projected image, but you will be able to point to the offending words or passage. Make provision, in this case, for an illuminated blackboard, if possible, so that you can use it while the image of the page is still being projected in the darkened room.

Because the object of this exercise is not so much to arrive at an improved version of the faulty paper as to teach general principles of style, work out beforehand which of the corrections you will spend most time on and ensure that each one either makes a major point or can be related to one of the Four Rules already enunciated. It is discouraging for students to watch you make many minor corrections that seem to have no general application and no relationship to an over-all scheme. For the same reason, control the extensive discussion that inevitably results from this exercise in such a way that the framework of principles and the categorization of errors remain clearly in the foreground. Defend nothing on the grounds of personal taste; if you can refer neither to a principle of scientific style nor to an unequivocal rule of grammar, concede the point. Try to avoid being either pedantic or apologetic.

Your students will have detected and corrected many of the errors already, and will be heartened by seeing you treat them in the same way. Other points will be new to them. In some places, content yourself with indicating what is wrong, and why—and let your students provide the correction. As a final exercise on Style, have them extend and complete the editing of the assignment in the light of what they have learned during this session, and hand in their final version of it a few days later. A brief examination of these versions will show where each student still needs guidance or further study, and you will be able to direct him to appropriate authorities. Try not to involve yourself in detailed correction at this stage; such correction will be much more telling in the revised draft of the student's Major Assignment, to which he is more deeply committed both intellectually and emotionally.

STEP 20:   [Fourth Session]

You may or may not consider a fourth Style Session to be necessary; but it is wise to allow for it if possible. Your students will almost certainly be bursting with questions: they may want you to explain one of the principles again or to provide a more elegant solution than theirs to one of the problems in the editing assignment. On your side, you may want to elucidate something that they apparently have not grasped. Perhaps you should stress again the enjoyment and profit to be gained from careful reading of the books in the book list (p. 56) and the importance of *critical* reading of everything that comes their way for the continuing development of good scientific style.

After the editing assignment and subsequent session(s), return to the sequence of steps, in which *Step 20: Polishing the Style* has been a lengthy one, and fill in the details of Steps 21–25 as indicated in Chapter 8. You may wish to end your course there, or to extend it with the material in Chapter 9 or any of the chapters in the second half of this book that fit both the needs of your students and your own time schedule.

7

Editing Assignments

In this chapter three examples of "editing assignments" are given. For instructions on how to prepare and use such assignments, see Chapter 6.

None of the examples carries a heading abstract. Advise students, when you give them the faulty text to edit, to read the whole paper through and write an abstract of it—in order to establish for themselves what the paper actually has to say—before they begin to correct the style.

ASSIGNMENT 1: FAULTY TEXT

THE PROBLEM[1] OF LIPID PEROXIDES AS ARTIFACTS
IN HUMAN AORTA LIPIDS

N. B. Gee, P. D. Cue, and S. O. Hess

INTRODUCTION

It has been suggested by some researchers[2] (1) that
peroxides of lipids that are formed in the arterial
wall conceivably[3] have a possible[3] role in causing[4]
atherogenesis. This postulate has been widely
accepted as a reasonable one, in view of the ready
capability of breakdown of these compounds with the
initiation of progressive chain reactions and the
formation of a variety of[5] potentially toxic
secondary[6] products.

In this connection,[7] the destructive effects of
lipid peroxides on serum β—lipoproteins (2) and
on the SH group in proteins (3) have been noted[8].

---

[1] Word frequently misused in scientific articles. Real chemical substances such
as peroxides cannot be a "problem": the problem may be where they come
from, how to get rid of them, or how to prevent their formation. Often a
scientist will call something a problem which is actually a phenomenon ("The
Problem of Adhesive Selectivity in Cellular Interactions"). The problem he
has in mind, of course, is how to account for the phenomenon, but this is
beside the point. (Rule 2)

[2] "by some researchers" redundant. (Rule 1)

[3] Triple hedging: "suggested" is already tentative enough; "conceivably" and
"possible" weaken rather than strengthen the effect. (Rule 1)

[4] This word should never be thrown about incautiously. Here, it can simply be
dropped (if we remember the precise meaning of "genesis"). (Rule 2)

[5] Common circumlocution. (Rule 1)

[6] The force of "secondary" is obscure. What is the difference from "primary"
products? Are *only* the secondary products potentially toxic? These questions
expose the word as verbiage. (Rule 2)

[7] A weak connective, to be used only in desperation. Should a new paragraph
be started here? (Rule 1)

[8] This prissy word warns the alert reviser that there is something wrong: probably the "real" verb is hidden in some other word. And it is: "destructive."
(Rule 1)

ASSIGNMENT 1: IMPROVED TEXT

THE ARTIFACTUAL NATURE OF LIPID PEROXIDES DETECTED IN EXTRACTS OF HUMAN AORTA

E. X. Celsior and I. M. Provement

INTRODUCTION

It has been suggested (1) that lipid peroxides formed in the arterial wall are[1] active in atherogenesis. The[2] suggestion[3] has been widely accepted as reasonable, since these compounds break down[4] readily, initiating chain reactions[5] as they do so and forming various products that are potentially toxic[6]. For example, lipid peroxides[7] denature[8] serum β-lipoproteins (2) and attack the SH group of proteins (3). When vitamin E-deficient

General. A good title should be short, informative, and precise, and much anxious thought should go into it both before the paper is outlined and after the final draft is ready.

This one is far from elegant. It starts with the article "The," which can often be dispensed with but which is essential here. It contains the warning word "nature." Re-examine the title after you have read the article, and decide whether it conveys the message exactly. If it does, further elegance need not be sought.

[1] How clear the air becomes when the triple hedges are torn down! But note: there is no diminution of caution. (Rule 1)

[2] Eliminate "this" whenever it is not strictly necessary. (Rule 1)

[3] A "postulate" is something assumed without proof. (Rule 2)

[4] Trapped verb in the abstract noun "breakdown" has been released; note increase of comprehensibility. (Rule 3)

[5] A chain reaction is always "progressive." (Rule 2)

[6] "Potentially toxic" rearranged to a position of emphasis. Word order is a subject for discussion on Further Points of Style; see Lucas pp. 39–41, 231 ff.

[7] No change in direction of ideas, hence no new paragraph.

[8] When the trapped verb in "destructive" has been released, the author finds that he wants to be more specific about the *kind* of destruction.

Lipid peroxides appear in rat adipose and muscular tissues under conditions[9] of vitamin E deficiency and during the application[10] of a diet rich in polyunsaturated fats (4), and the formation[11] of "ceroid" in atherosclerotic arteries has been attributed to the autoxidation[11] and polymerization[11] of the unsaturated lipids which they contain (5).

Following[12] the results of Lufton and Sowerby (1), the atherogenic role for lipid peroxides has been on firmer ground[13]. They[14] found an increasing[15] degree of lipid peroxidation in human aortic wall, positively correlated with the degree of atherosclerosis. It struck[16] us that the lipid extracting method[17] used by them, namely mixing with anhydrous sodium sulfate by means of a chop-knife and extraction of the mixture with chloroform, was liable[18] to effect[19] the artifactual formation of lipid peroxides from unsaturated lipids, and we undertook reinvestigation[20] of the lipid[21] peroxide[21] occurrence[21] problem employing extraction[20] at greatly

---

[9] Warning word: the statement containing it may be vague. (Rule 1)

[10] Is a diet "applied" or "fed"? (Rule 2)

[11] Abstract nouns containing hidden or trapped verbs. (Rule 3)

[12] Eliminate "following" wherever possible. Sometimes it is a dangling participle, sometimes a vogue-word substituting for the simple "after." Here, as in many instances, it leads to the hilarious suspicion that the atherogenic role is following the results around (see Fowler: *Following*). (Rule 2)

[13] The metaphors "role" and "firm ground" are not dead enough to allow of mixing (see Orwell, G., 1947, "Politics and the English Language," *The New Republic*). (Rule 2)

[14] Antecedent ambiguous ("results," "Lufton and Sowerby," "peroxides"?) (Rule 2)

[15] Increasing with what? (Rule 2)

[16] Inappropriately colloquial.

[17] The scientific literature is riddled with this Germanic construction. In English it is sheer nonsense: what lipid ever extracted a method? Who ever asked in a drugstore for a coffee containing cup? (Rule 2)

[18] Anthropomorphic.

[19] An affected "warning word." (Rule 3)

[20] Abstract nouns for pomposity's sake. (Rule 3)

[21] Nouns clustering (Rule 4) around the foolish "problem."

rats are fed[9] a diet rich in polyunsaturated fats, lipid peroxides appear in their adipose and muscular tissues (4); similarly, it is thought, unsaturated lipids present in atherosclerotic arteries may autoxidize[10] and then polymerize[10] to form[10] "ceroid"[11] (5).

Lufton and Sowerby (1) provided some evidence[12] for the atherogenic role of lipid peroxides. They showed that the content of peroxides[13] in lipids extracted from the human aortic wall[14] increased[15] with the degree of atherosclerosis. They[16] extracted the lipids, however, by mixing the tissue[17], exposed to the air[18], with anhydrous sodium sulfate and extracting the mixture with chloroform at room temperature[18]. These treatments may have caused the artifactual formation, by oxidation[19], of peroxides from unsaturated lipids during the extraction. We have therefore reopened the question of whether lipid peroxides[20] occur in aorta lipids, using an-

[9] Reserve the frequently substituted "administered" for occasions when unnatural forms of feeding (e.g., stomach tube) have been used. (Rule 1)

[10] The trapped verbs "form," "autoxidize," and "polymerize" have been released. Note increase in simplicity and vigor. (Rule 3)

[11] "Ceroid" has been brought to a position of emphasis.

[12] The cliché "on firmer ground" has been substituted by the unobjectionable "evidence."

[13] The corrected version is more specific, i.e., avoids the abstract "peroxidation" and speaks of "peroxides." (Rule 3)

[14] Phrase expanded for clarity and precision.

[15] Simplification of "positively correlates" with no loss of meaning.

[16] This time "they" can open the sentence because antecedent is unambiguous. The construction, moreover, is now parallel to that of the preceding sentence.

[17] "the tissue" has been added for clarification (answering the question "mixing what? Lipids?"). (Rule 2)

[18] "exposed to the air" and "at room temperature" have been added to bring out why the method might have led to oxidation.

[19] Specific and informative expansion of "formation."

[20] Breaking up the noun cluster to give "the problem of the lipid peroxides" reveals that it is not so much a problem as a question; releasing the hidden verb "occur" produced the further simplification. Notice that the verb "occur," so often a colorless nothing-word, is here accurate and meaningful.

reduced[22] temperatures in order to achieve[23]
avoidance[20] of that possibility[20].

MATERIALS AND METHODS

Aortas were obtained at 6–12 hr autopsy[24] at the
University Hospital, Barchester. The classification
of each as regards stage of atherosclerosis (0, I,
II, or III) was done as described by Gee et al. (6),
examining[25] the appearance of the intima, after
which the adventitia (outer layer)[26] was rapidly but
carefully[27] removed.

The intima and media aorta preparations[28] were
immediately put into a mixture of methanol and
chloroform, approximately[29] 100 volumes, 2:1 (v/v).
Storage took place at −20 °C. Following[30] the lapse
of a given time (a period of one week was
approximated[31]) the lower chloroform containing
layer[32] was separated and analysis was performed
on it.

[22] More orotundity. (Rule 3)

[23] Warning Word. (Rule 3)

[24] This kind of shorthand "lab slang" seems very convenient to the speaker, but
as with most alluring things, the price is high. Readers should never be subjected to it, for they cannot demand that the authors explain themselves.
Listeners often misunderstand it, because the words have (for them) an obvious
meaning which is *not* that intended. Lastly, the speaker may confuse himself
through constant repetition of a phrase without considering its meaning.
(Rule 2)

[25] Dangling participle. (Rule 2)

[26] Judgment: Know your audience. Readers of this paper can be expected to
know what arterial adventitia is.

[27] All manipulations described in scientific papers are assumed to have been
careful. (Rule 2)

[28] Noun cluster obscures meaning. (Rule 4)

[29] Grandilingua for "about." (Rule 1)

[30] Warning word ending in "ing." (Rule 2)

[31] Prime example of complickese. (Rule 1)

[32] That coffee containing cup again. (Rule 2)

aerobic extraction at much lower temperatures in order to minimize oxidation.

MATERIALS AND METHODS

Aortic tissue[21]

Aortas were obtained at autopsy, within 6–12 hr of death[22], at the University Hospital, Barchester. Aortas were classified[23] as being at stage 0, I, II, or III of atherosclerosis[24] according to the appearance of the intima (6), and the adventitia was rapidly removed.

Each preparation, comprising intima and media[25], was immediately submerged[26] in about 100 volumes of methanol–chloroform 2:1 (v/v)[27] and stored[28] at −20 °C. After about one week the lower (lipid–containing)[29] layer was separated and its peroxide content was determined[30].

---

[21] Subheadings inserted as signposts.

[22] The shorthand jargon "6–12 hr autopsy" has been expanded to be comprehensible and precise. (Rule 2)

[23] Hidden verb "classify" released; colorless verb "done" eliminated. (Rule 3)

[24] Phrase condensed by elimination of unnecessary words. (Rule 1)

[25] More information given; also, more precise in making clear that the preparation consists of one piece of tissue (therefore singular verb).

[26] Diction: descriptive verb replaces colorless one.

[27] The "100 volumes" separated from "(v/v)" for clarity.

[28] Brevity achieved by release of hidden verb "store." (Rule 2)

[29] This clarifying adjective would not be necessary for the "in-group" but helps a wider circle of readers without offending anyone.

[30] Abstract noun "analysis" replaced by precise phrase. (Rule 3)

In some cases[33] the aortic material was further
extracted with the same solvent at room temperature
with stirring, and subsequently at the reflux
temperature. The further yield of lipid was never
more than half that initially extracted; the
peroxide value of this extract was negligible, thus
proving[34] that extraction at the lower temperature
did extract peroxides effectively.

To determine[35] the oxidizability of lipid while
it[36] is still contained in the tissue, a few aorta
preparations were halved and one part exposed[37] to
the atmosphere at room temperature (25°C) for 30
minutes before extraction, while[38] the other was
extracted immediately after removal of the
adventitia.

Aliquots of the extracts were taken to dryness in
tared glass shells for analysis[39] of total lipid
content[39] and determination of peroxide contents
were[40] conducted on similar aliquots.

---

[33] Warning word: "cases" (see Gowers, *Plain Words*). In medical work especially
the word has special connotations and should be avoided where these are not
desired. In more general usage ("in the case of sunflower seeds") it can often
be omitted altogether. (Rule 1)

[34] Dangling participle.

[35] Dangling infinitive (rarer than dangling participle, but still common). Subject
of the verb "determine" is the investigator, subject of the main clause is "aorta
preparations."

[36] Antecedent ambiguous ("oxidizability"?). (Rule 2)

[37] Incorrect omission of the auxiliary. Verb needed, "was." Grammatically
implied, "were." (Rule 2)

[38] Note correct usage of "while:" true simultaneity of action here. "Whereas" is
preferable when contrast only is to be conveyed. (Rule 2)

[39] "Analysis" implies a fractionation, which is not employed here. Hence Rule
2 is violated.

[40] Incorrect number of the verb, because of "contamination" by the nearest
noun. Always examine what is the subject of each verb. (Rule 2)

Some of the aortic material[31] was further extracted with the same solvent mixture[32] at room temperature with stirring, and subsequently under reflux[33]. The further yield of lipid never exceeded[34] one half of[35] that initially extracted; the lipid peroxide value of the second extract was negligible. These findings quashed the possibility that peroxides were not efficiently extracted at the lower temperature and permitted conclusions to be drawn from examination of the low-temperature extract exclusively[36].

To determine[37] how easily lipid is oxidized while it is still contained in the tissue, we divided a few aorta preparations into two. One part was exposed to the atmosphere at room temperature (25°C)[38] for 30 minutes before extraction, while the other was extracted immediately after removal of the adventitia.

Total lipid concentration of each extract was determined by drying[39] a portion in a tared glass

---

[31] One way to eliminate "case."

[32] Slight increase in precision. (Rule 2)

[33] Slightly more concise. (Rule 1)

[34] Diction: a precise, meaningful verb has replaced three colorless words.

[35] *Expansion* for clarity!

[36] In order to express the train of thought fully, the writer has had to expand his statement. Conciseness is not invariably ideal.

Some results are mentioned in this Methods section. This is sometimes inevitable and should not be shunned if their inclusion clarifies procedure or experimental design. The reason for their appearance "out of order" should be made amply clear: another function of the phrase marked[36].

Furthermore, the method for determining peroxide value has not yet been described; if subheadings are used the reader will rapidly observe that this description is to be provided shortly.

[37] Infinitive no longer dangles.

[38] "at 25°C" would be briefer, but would jettison an important point, namely the implication that other investigators working at room temperature inadvertently allowed autoxidation to take place. On the other hand, room temperature must be specified because this varies from place to place.

[39] Dangling participle, of the least objectionable kind.

Iodimetric lipid peroxide determination[41] is conveniently precise, and accurate for samples containing more than 50 μeq of peroxides (7), but as generally applied it is too insensitive for aortic extracts[42]. The microiodimetric procedure of Proudie and Slope (8) is approximately 2 orders of magnitude[43] more sensitive than earlier methods and enabled[44] results to be obtained on extracts from single aortas. The procedure was as described (8)[45].

RESULTS

The results are shown in Table I. The number of values obtained for less diseased aortas is small, for the reasons given below. Examination of the table reveals that[46] the peroxide values obtained[47] are all very[48] much lower than those of Lufton and Sowerby (1), which ranged from 3, at their so-called[49] Stage I of atherosclerosis, to 17, at their Stage V, μeq/g lipid[50]. None[51] of our values exceeded 2 and most of them[52] were less than 1 μeq/g.

[41] Cluster; slight pause necessary to grasp meaning. (Rule 4)

[42] What differentiates aortic extracts from other extracts is not immediately clear.

[43] Grandiloquence, see Baker. (Rule 1)

[44] Although Webster now admits the usage in which "enable" is synonymous with "allow," it remains more elegant to enable only persons to do things, not to enable things to be done.

[45] The principle of a method should always be succinctly stated even though a reference to its extended description is given.

[46] All words before this point in this sentence are redundant. (Rule 1)

[47] Redundant. (Rule 1)

[48] This word is used oftener than is warranted in scientific literature. (Rule 1)

[49] This word has derogatory overtones and is best avoided.

[50] The clumsy word-order is not redeemed by a plethora of commas.

[51] The perspicacious reader will observe that if the values in Table I are correct, either this statement is wrong or the distribution of values was skew.

[52] Redundant. (Rule 1)

shell; the peroxide concentration of another portion was measured[40] by micro-iodimetry[41].

Determination of lipid peroxides by micro-iodimetry[42]

The iodimetric method for determination of lipid peroxides is convenient, precise, and accurate for samples containing more than 50 μeq of peroxides (7), but as generally applied it is too insensitive for use with extracts of single aortas[43], which usually contain (especially if they are relatively free from atherosclerotic lesions) a small total amount of lipid which itself contains little peroxide. The micro-iodimetric method of Proudie and Slope (8) is about 100 times[44] as sensitive as earlier methods and was successfully applied. It employs electrometric titration of iodine liberated from iodide by the peroxides in acid solution.

RESULTS

The results are shown in Tables I and II[45]. The number of values obtained for less diseased aortas is small, for the reasons given below. The peroxide values in Table I are all much lower than those of Lufton and Sowerby (1), which ranged from 3 ("Stage I") to 17 ("Stage V") μeq/g lipid. Only one of our values was higher than 2 and most were below 1 μeq/g. There was no obvious correlation

---

[40] The hidden verb to be released was "determine" but because this has been used earlier in the sentence, "measure" is substituted for variety.

[41] More information provided, and a link with the next section results.

[42] Subheading for guidance of the reader.

[43] Inclusion of an important point (single aorta) here clarifies the thought. There is then no need to repeat the words later.

[44] A straightforward number is almost always to be preferred to "orders of magnitude."

[45] The data have been separated into two tables because there were two points to be made. See notes under the tables.

TABLE I

Peroxide values

Tissue exposed to air[a]			Tissue not exposed before extraction[a]		
Stage of athero-sclerosis	Tissue No.	Peroxide Content	Stage of athero-sclerosis	Tissue No.	Peroxide Content
		μeq/g			μeq/g
III[b]	21[c]	2.62	III[b]	1–13,20,21,22[c]	1.26 ± 0.91[d]
III[b]	22	1.64	II[b]	14–17	0.84 ± 0.30
I[b]	23	1.81	I[b]	18,23	1.18 ± 0.57[e]
			0[b]	19	0.41

General. Design of table is confused. One realizes this when he tries to expand the title to be informative: such a long title results that it is clear that two tables are needed, each to show a different point.

[a] Since one reads from left to right, it is normally better to show controls on the left.

[b] Similarly, as one reads downwards, it is usually best to show controls, or less-diseased samples, at the top.

[c] The numbers designating individual samples of aortic tissue are of no assistance to the reader unless he can compare values for any one tissue in different places in the table. Here individual values have, in the right-hand half of the table, been buried in means. No direct comparison is possible, as it is in Table II in the improved version.

[d] There is no indication whether this is Standard Deviation or Standard Error of the Mean. This must always be stated explicitly, together with the number of observations (readily deduced, in this case, from penultimate column).

[e] When there are only two values, it is simply foolish to report them thus.

    Table I also shows that[53] when tissue was exposed to the air at 25 °C the peroxide value was increased 2–3 times (tissues 21–23), suggesting[25] very[48] strongly that in this situation[54] lipid peroxides are formed through an artifactual conversion[55] of the lipids before they are extracted. Since some exposure

[53] All words up to this point redundant. (Rule 1)

[54] Warning word: often indicates that the writer is not thinking. Here the phrase can be deleted altogether.

[55] Circumlocution.

TABLE I

Peroxide values of lipids from aortas at different
stages of atherosclerosis

Stage of Atherosclerosis	No. of aortas	Peroxide Content
		μeq/g
0	1	0.41
I	2	0.61, 1.75
II	4	0.84 ± 0.30*
III	16	1.26 ± 0.91*

* Standard Deviation

TABLE II

Effect on lipid peroxide levels of exposing tissue
to air before extraction of the lipids

Aorta No.	Stage of Atherosclerosis	Peroxide Content	
		Extracted immediately	Exposed*
		μeq/g	μeq/g
1	I	0.61	1.81
2	III	0.81	1.64
3	III	0.80	2.62

* For 30 min at 25 °C

General. The titles and layout expose experimental design completely to a reader who has not yet looked at the text; this reader is also given crucial information succinctly in the footnote to Table II.

between peroxide content and stage of atherosclerosis[46].

Exposure of the tissue to air at room temperature
increased the peroxide value 2–3 times (Table II),
which strongly suggests[47] that lipid peroxides are
easily formed artifactually[48] before the lipids can

[46] An extra, important conclusion has been added.
[47] Replaces dangling participle.
[48] Replaces circumlocutory phrase.

cannot be avoided during manipulation[56] at autopsy
and during removal of adventitia, all values in
Table I are likely[57] too high. Based on[58] this
result, and coupled with the fact that even these
sensitive methods do not have the ability to yield
an accurate result on the small amounts of lipid
obtainable from Stage 0 or I aortas, the project
of comparing peroxide contents of aortas with
varying[59] degrees of atherosclerosis has been
abandoned at the present time[60].

DISCUSSION

If, as seems likely from these results, the high
values of Lufton and Sowerby (1) for the aorta
lipid peroxide content[61] were due to artifactual
formation of peroxides [during tissue preparation
and possibly during the extraction of the lipids]*,
[the question arises]*, why did these authors
obtain a correlation of peroxide content with
atherosclerosis? [At the time of their investigation
(1951) it was not known that]* the arterial lipid
unsaturation index[61] increases with increasing
degree of atherosclerosis. This increasing
unsaturation, most striking in the cholesteryl
esters, was shown by Gee et al. (6) [with the aid
of gas–liquid chromatography]*. Furthermore, the

[56] Redundant polysyllable. (Rule 1)
[57] Adjective, now accepted by Webster as adverb, still grates on some people in
   this usage.
[58] Beware: this phrase is often discovered to harbor a dangling past participle,
   as here. (Rule 2)
[59] Frequently, and shamefully, misused. "Varying" is a continuous process and
   the word should not be confused with "various" or "different." (Rule 2)
[60] Redundant. (Rule 1)
[61] Noun cluster. (Rule 4)
* There are few stylistic or grammatical errors in the Discussion; it is made too
   long not by roundabout phraseology but by the inclusion of irrelevancies,
   marked [ ]*.

be extracted. Since some exposure is inevitable
during autopsy and removal of adventitia, all
values in Table I are likely to be[49] too high. For
this reason, and because even these sensitive
methods are incapable[50] of giving an accurate result
on the small amounts of lipid that can be extracted[51]
from Stage 0 or I aortas, the project of comparing
peroxide contents of aortas with differing[52] degrees
of atherosclerosis has been abandoned.

DISCUSSION[53]

If the peroxides measured in lipid extracts from
the arterial wall are artifacts, how can we
explain Lufton and Sowerby's findings (1) that
the peroxide content is correlated with degree of
atherosclerosis? It has recently been discovered
(6) that arterial lipids become progressively more
unsaturated with increasing degree of atherosclerosis. Among the lipid classes, cholesteryl
esters show the most striking increase in
unsaturation, and the proportion of cholesteryl
esters relative to the other lipids also rises
(9, 10). The more atherosclerotic the aorta,
therefore, the more susceptible will its lipids be

---

[49] Note insertion. The correction can sometimes be made by substituting "probably" for "likely."

[50] Replaces roundabout phrase.

[51] Substituted for "obtainable" for variety: "incapable . . . obtainable" had an
ugly jingle (fine point, can be omitted).

[52] Another way of correcting "varying."

[53] The argument here is tighter because the writer has eliminated irrelevant
information and has worked on his connectives.

proportion of cholesteryl esters relative to the
other lipids rises also, [as has long been recog-
nized]* (9, 10). The atherosclerotic aorta therefore
bears an increasingly oxidizable lipid load, and
this would be sufficiently explanatory[62] of the
results obtained.

    We should like[63] to point out, however, that
lipid peroxidation may still be involved somehow
in the inception of atherosclerosis or in forwarding
its progress. Although only small amounts of lipid
peroxides were found, they[64] might be genuine
components of the tissue. The possibility also
exists that more were present in the living patient,
but decomposed between the time of death and the
autopsy. Their very decomposition in the living
tissue might have been the cause of atherosclerotic
changes. But it is not our opinion[65] that measurement
of peroxides in necropsy material can elucidate
this problem[66].

REFERENCES

1. L. Lufton[a] and J. Sowerby. 1952. Acta pathol.
   et.[b] microbiology[c] 30:492.

---

[62] Verb here is hidden in an adjective for a change; the resultant construction is
no less stilted.

[63] This kind of absurd conditional should be avoided: the authors *are* pointing
it out. (Rule 2)

[64] Is antecedent "amounts" or "peroxides"? (Rule 2)

[65] Circumlocution. (Rule 1)

[66] Warning word: note again how it enables an author to be vague. What, of the
several speculative statements in preceding sentences, does the author regard
as "the problem?"

If you wish, you can use the editing assignment to provide instruction on giving
references correctly, in a consistent style. The basis for analyzing these muddled
references is the "correct form" given on the opposite page, in the Improved
Text. The deviations above are as follows:

[a] Initial precedes surname of first author.

[b] Period placed after a word that is not an abbreviation.

[c] Written out in full, incorrectly (obvious from the rest that journal title is in
Latin).

to oxidation during dissection; this effectively explains the observed correlation.

Our results do not exclude the possibility that lipid peroxides play a role in atherogenesis or in the development of atherosclerosis. The small amounts found may not be entirely artifactual. Furthermore, lipid peroxides present in vivo may decompose between death and autopsy. More importantly, they may have formed earlier in the patient's life and subsequently decomposed, with the undesirable consequences mentioned in the Introduction. We do not believe, however, that their possible role in atherosclerosis has been or can be established by examination of the lipids after death.

REFERENCES

1. Lufton, L., and J. Sowerby. 1952. <u>Acta Pathol</u>. <u>Microbiol</u>. 30: 492.

References. Note consistency of styling. This is, unfortunately, different for each journal; the style of the chosen journal must be rigorously followed. For abbreviation of journal titles, the American Standard (see *Biological Abstracts,* 48 (24), 15 December 1967) is now recommended.

2. Robarts, M., D. O. Omnium[d] and G. Dumbello,[d] 1961. J. Perfect Res.[d] 2:631.
3. Neroni, M. V. 1953. Bull. Soc. ital. sper. Biol.[e] 92:16.
4. De Courcy, E. 1963. Extrait de[f] Bull. Soc. Chem.[g] France 116:214.
5. Hartletop, M. O. J. Gerontol.[h] 63, 321 (1958)[i].
6. Gee, N. B., Whiz, A. C.[j] and W. A. Goof[k] Scalpel i:137[m], 1960.
7. Eaxes, J. and Buffle, R. (ed.) Organic Peroxide Analysis 1:376, 1856[n].
8. Proudie, M. B., and O. Slope. (1964). J. W. M.[p] 3:423.
9. Dunstable, E., et al.[q] Biochem.[g] Biophys. Acta 74:111, 1957.
10. Doppelganger,[r] D., and D. Winterreise. Z. Phys.[s] Chem. 216 (1915) 984.

[d] Comma omitted; comma substituted for period after "Dumbello"; underscoring omitted.
[e] Arbitrary decisions on capitalization of each abbreviation.
[f] Blind copying from the heading on the reprint.
[g] Misspelled foreign word that is similar to English equivalent.
[h] Underscoring omitted.
[i] Incorrect form for volume, page, year.
[j] Initials should precede name of second author.
[k] Period omitted.
[m] Last digit of page number dropped.
[n] A multitude of faults, including misspelling of author's name, grossly wrong date, the treatment of a book as a journal, and the omission of the publisher and place of publication.
[p] Unpardonable to refer to a journal by initials only.
[q] All authors must be given.
[r] Foreigners like to receive all their diacritical marks.
[s] Complete confusion possible as a result of wrong abbreviation.

2. Robarts, M., D. O. Omnium, and G. Dumbello. 1961. J. Perfect Res. 2: 631.
3. Neroni, M. V. 1953. Bull. Soc. Ital. Sper. Biol. 92: 16.
4. De Courcy, E. 1963. Bull. Soc. Chim. Fr. 116: 214.
5. Hartletop, M. O. 1958. J. Gerontol. 63: 321.
6. Gee, N. B., A. C. Whiz, and W. A. Goof. 1960. Scalpel. i: 1378.
7. Eames, J. 1956. In Organic Peroxide Analysis. Sir Raffle Buffle, editor. Cathedral Publishers, Barchester. 1: 376.
8. Proudie, M. B., and O. Slope. 1964. J. Workable Methods. 3: 423.
9. Dunstable, E., F. Gresham, and M. Thorne. 1957. Biochim. Biophys. Acta. 74: 111.
10. Doppelgänger, D., and D. Winterreise. 1915. Hoppe-Seyler's Z. Physiol. Chem. 216: 984.

Reconsideration of Title

Now that you have read the paper, do you think any of the following titles is better than the one suggested?

1. Evidence that Lipid Peroxides Detected in Extracts of Human Aorta Are Artifacts.
2. Lipid Peroxides Found in Human Aorta Lipids Are Artifacts.
3. Are Lipid Peroxides in Extracts of Human Aorta Artifacts?
4. Artifactual Formation of Peroxides in Lipids Extracted from Human Aorta.
5. Peroxide Formation in Lipids of Human Aorta.
6. Peroxide Formation in Lipids Extracted from Human Aorta.

ASSIGNMENT 2: FAULTY TEXT

AN EXAMINATION OF THE MEASURES TAKEN BY PHYSICAL FITNESS TESTS AND THEIR INFLUENCE ON FINAL TEST SCORES

Woody Lissen and Way Behind

INTRODUCTION

Cardiovascular-function and general bodily efficiency relationships[1] have formed the subject of a great deal of research[2] in order to gauge[3] the general health of individuals. Workers in the physical fitness field have often been puzzled by the lack of agreement in results shown by tests all purporting to measure this[4] general trait.

This study attempted to separate the similarities and dissimilarities[5] underlying measurements which were[6] derived from several such tests, all of[6] which have found support in one or more of the services. The tests in question[6] were the Behnke step-up test (1), the Harvard step-up test (2), and the Schneider index of physical fitness (3).

General note. This is a much shorter example than the preceding one and is not intended to be criticized for lack of data or documentation for the conclusions. No tables are provided.

Title. Too general, and unnecessarily wordy. If the type of examination were precisely specified, the phrase "their influence in final test scores" could be eliminated.

[1] Impressive noun cluster. (Rule 4)
[2] The alert reviser will detect wordiness by noticing the number of words without much content: "formed," "subject," "great deal."
[3] Dangling infinitive, not disguised by "in order."
[4] Antecedent unclear.
[5] One word (e.g., disparity) is better. (Rule 1)
[6] Awkward and unnecessary. Why not simply "measurements derived?" The addition of such unnecessary material makes for a turgid and dreary style. (Rule 1)

ASSIGNMENT 2: IMPROVED TEXT

STATISTICAL EVALUATION OF THREE[1] TESTS OF PHYSICAL FITNESS[2] UTILIZED BY THE ARMED FORCES

Heed More and H. E. Ketchup

INTRODUCTION

Physical fitness tests rely on the relationship between cardiovascular function and bodily efficiency to provide an index of general health. Students of human physiology are disturbed by the poor correlations among tests that are supposed to measure a single characteristic, physical fitness. The study summarized here[3] attempts to explain the disparity among three fitness tests currently utilized in the Armed Forces: the Behnke step up test (1), the Harvard step-up test (2), and the Schneider index of physical fitness (3).

[1] Since there are many tests of physical fitness in use, the title should indicate the study's limitations.

[2] The title could end here, but the additional information furnished by the third line indicates the relevance of the study and narrows its application—for instance, the Director of Activities at Leisure World need not have a copy in his library!

[3] Let the reader know at the onset that the paper is a summary so that he will not expect a great deal of detail. (Consideration for audience)

THE TESTS[7]

The 120 randomly selected subjects were chosen by
separating from a main group of approximately 400
men (enlisted candidates for submarine training)
the occupants of chairs which had been previously
secretly marked. Strict control[8] of the lives of the
subjects was maintained[9] by regulating[10] their
activities during an experimental period which
lasted for three days. They were quartered in a
special barracks and ate at a separate mess.

Correlation[11] exhibited by the tests utilized in
this study[12] was found to be poor. The endurance
phase of the Behnke test had a correlation of 0.231
with the Harvard test and 0.038 with the Schneider
index. The two latter tests had correlations of
0.282 and 0.284 for the cardiovascular phase of
the Behnke test[13,14]. Thus, this particular study[12]
gives support to claims of other studies (4,5)
that various tests all of which[12] claim to measure
the general trait of physical fitness show a poor
correlation.

To explain[15] this noticeable lack of correlation,
it was decided that the data would be appraised
further by means of the Adjutant General's Office
(Army) – modified Thurstone Group Centroid
method[1].

---

[7] Too vague to serve as a guide to the reader and incorrect to boot. The section
doesn't describe the tests themselves but rather the general procedure. (Rule 2)

[8] What aspects of the subjects' lives were "strictly controlled"? (Rule 2)

[9] Warning word. Verb needed: "controlled" or "regulated." (Rule 3)

[10] Dangling participle

[11] Too vague. Correlation with what? (Rule 2)

[12] Unnecessary; simply adds to wordiness. (Rule 1)

[13] Don't switch order of comparison; this makes it harder for reader to follow.

[14] A general statement of the low correlation is sufficient in a summary. Incidentally, nowhere in this text is the reader informed that the paper is merely a
summary.

[15] Dangling infinitive.

PROCEDURE

The sample of 120 men was randomly selected from
400 enlisted candidates processed through the
Submarine Training School[4]. The fitness tests were
part of a battery of measures being considered for
their possible value in selecting men for submarine
duty[5]. The tests were administered in random order,
one on each afternoon of a 3-day experimental period
during which the daily program and diets of the
subjects were strictly regulated.

STATISTICAL ANALYSIS[6]

Correlation coefficients were determined for 35
variables (see Table 1)* selected from the test
measures. The poor correlation exhibited between
the final scores of the three tests (0.282 for
Behnke and Harvard, 0.284 for Behnke and Schneider,
0.082 for Harvard and Schneider) was in keeping
with the results of other studies (4,5).

The data were further examined by a modified (6)
Thurstone group centroid method (7) of factor

---

[4] Sufficient to give the idea that the total group was large enough for the 120
subjects to be representative; unnecessary methodological detail eliminated.

[5] This will tell the reader why the tests were considered important enough to proceed with an involved analysis when initial results were not encouraging.

[6] Another heading here helps the reader.

* See footnote on p. 78; the tables in this example are imaginary.

Results of the factorial appraisal of physical fitness data[16] will be discussed in as general terms as possible[17] for the benefit of the nonstatistical reader.

RESULTS AND DISCUSSION

If occasionally this general discussion of statistical results gives rise to the impression that some of the utterances are "ex cathedra"[18], it is emphasized that there is a statistical justification for all conclusions drawn, as indicated by available verifications presented in the table of intercorrelations, the table of factor loadings, and the table of residuals[19].

This paper does not attempt to delineate the physiological functions which should be included in an estimate of the general trait of physical fitness and thus infringe on the rights of specialists in the area of physical fitness[20]. There is no implication intended that the functions isolated by this study are the only valuable components in gauging physical fitness but rather that they are the only physiological functions actually measured by the tests investigated[21]. When there has been[22] substantial agreement among

[16] Long, unnecessary, and repetitious. (Rule 1)

[17] Why not simply "in general terms"? (Rule 1)

[18] Pompous. The second part of the sentence documents the findings. In general, Latin phrases (including *vide supra* and *circa*) should be regarded as "warning words" and translated.

[19] Why not simply refer to the tables by number? If the reader is not statistically oriented, such words as factor loadings and residuals won't mean anything. (Rule 1)

[20] First, let's tell the reader what the analysis shows. This section is really *Discussion* not *Results*. In any case, it contains unnecessary verbiage.

[21] Faulty parallelism garbles the thought. Make into two sentences. (Rule 1)

[22] "There has been," "there is" often indicate that a passive voice is longing to be made active.

analysis, which attempts to explain the correlation coefficients in terms of a number of factors or underlying bases of association[7].

RESULTS AND RECOMMENDATIONS

Results will be presented in general terms for the convenience of readers who are not statistically oriented. Statistical verification of the statements can be found in Tables 2 and 3.

---

[7] Even the nonstatistical reader will want to know that correlation coefficients are the "raw data" for factor analysis.

specialists on just what components of physical
fitness should be represented in a physical
fitness[23] appraisal and just[24] how important each
component is relative[24] to such an estimate, test
scores may then be devised accordingly[24] to
represent these factors according to their appropriate percentages. The present study offers a
way in which an evaluation may be made to sys-
tematize fitness estimates for it has shown that
the tests investigated indicate that the influence
of physiological functions is a reflection of the
scoring method involved.

The following conclusions are drawn from the
findings of the present study[25]:
1. A basic resting pulse rate tends to characterize
each individual, tends to remain relatively constant
during any given day, appears to have[26] low day-to-
day reliability, and does not warrant making
predictions as to the results of readings taken on
the next or any other day[27].
2. Pulse response to prolonged violent exercise is
a basic physiological factor[28] and meaningful[29]
classification of individuals may be made[30] on the
basis of this factor.
3. Endurance time in seconds is a component[31] which
is a basic repeatable measure of individual
differences. Items contributing to the lowering
of endurance scores for a given individual are

---

[23] Repetitious.

[24] Examination of the meaning of these words reveals them to be redundant.

[25] Unnecessary verbiage. From what other study would they be drawn? (Rule 1)

[26] Excess of caution. (Rule 2)

[27] "low day-to-day reliability" is sufficient for the reader to draw a conclusion; rest of sentence unnecessary. Rule 2 might expose the fault, Rule 1 dictates deletion.

[28] What use do the test scores make of this factor? (Purpose of article forgotten)

[29] An overworked word. (Rule 2)

[30] Warning of a hidden verb. (Rule 3)

[31] Component of what? (Rule 2)

The principal findings were as follows:

1. A basic resting pulse rate characterizes each individual and tends to remain constant during any given day. However, day-to-day stability is low. If this measure is employed to estimate an individual's fitness for a particular task, it should be determined on the day of the assignment itself[8].

2. Pulse response to prolonged violent exercise is a basic physiological factor upon which a useful classification of individuals may be based. Unfortunately, scoring methods give little weight to this factor.

3. Endurance time in seconds is a basic repeatable measure of an individual's physical fitness. Items that contribute to the lowering of the endurance score include[9] (a) high increase in pulse rate

[8] Makes conclusion significant in terms of the purpose of the study.

[9] Word "include" is better than the "are" used on page 84. The implication is that still other factors may also be contributing. (Rule 2)

high increase in pulse rate following violent
exercise, slow return of pulse rate to normal after
exercise, high standing[32] in size-strength variables[32],
and increasing age.
4. A basic resting blood pressure level[33] is
characteristic of each individual and considerably[34]
influences his pulse reactions to exercise. This[35]
is also true of variability in blood pressure level
attributed to slight changes in environmental
conditions.
5. The advantage of the classification potential[36]
present in the measures taken and then not utilized
is not reflected in the final test scores for the
three tests.

[32] Meaning? Jargon like this should be eliminated by Step 24.

[33] Stacked modifiers. (Rule 4)

[34] Omit this "hedging" word; it belongs to a class of vague qualifiers of dubious
utility.

[35] Antecedent unclear. (Rule 2)

[36] This vogue-word is always suspect.

after violent exercise, (b) slow return of pulse
rate to normal after exercise, (c) high values in
measurements of the subject's size compared to his
strength, and (d) increasing age. We recommend that
upper age ceilings be established for any Armed
Services task that requires long maintenance of
violent bodily activity[8].
4. Each person has a characteristic blood pressure
level at rest and the reaction of his pulse rate to
exercise is related to this resting level. Variation
in level with slight changes in environmental
conditions is also characteristic of the individual.
Two of the tests investigated do not include
such measures; the other does include several
measures of blood pressure but virtually ignores
them in the scoring formula.
5. The fitness tests vary widely in the choice of
physiological functions which they actually measure
and in the contributions of these items to final
test scores.

DISCUSSION

Delineation of the physiological functions which
should be included in an estimate of the general
trait of "physical fitness" is outside our province.
We do not mean to imply that the functions isolated
by the factor analysis described are the only
components of value in gauging physical fitness.
The point is rather that they are the only physiological functions actually measured by the tests
named.
     The results clearly indicate that the tests
employed at present should be reevaluated and
systematized. For example, a certain pulse reaction
to prolonged violent exercise has been shown to be
characteristic of the individual. One of the tests

ASSIGNMENT 3: FAULTY TEXT

SOME STUDIES[1] ON A RAPID BIOASSAY MICROMETHOD[2]

A. Clodd

INTRODUCTION

Many authors, including[3] this laboratory (3)[4], have been engaged in the study of the identification[5] and detection[5] of specific[6] biologically active mole-

This editing assignment was kindly provided by Dr. William R. Lockhart, Department of Bacteriology, Iowa State University.

[1] See Step 22 (p. 104) on the need to avoid unnecessary words like these.

[2] Too vague. Students should read the whole article, then apply Rule 2 (Make Sure of the Meaning of Every Word) in making the title more precise.

[3] Can authors include a laboratory? (Rule 2)

[4] In this Assignment, a method of numbering references different from that in Assignment 1 is exemplified. The references here have been arranged alphabetically according to the first author's name and then numbered consecutively, instead of being numbered in the order of their appearance in the text. Both systems for citing references are actually used. What are the advantages of each?

[5] Abstract nouns derived from verbs. First target for revision! (Rule 3, Use Verbs Instead of Abstract Nouns)

[6] Overworked word, which has a definite and useful meaning, but which is often inserted to stop a gap in the author's thoughts.

[DISCUSSION—continued]

contains no estimate of this function, and the other two give little weight to it in their scoring methods. Moreover, resting blood pressure and variability in blood pressure are both components that can form the basis for useful classification, but two of the tests exclude these measures and the third virtually ignores their influence in the final test score.

When specialists in physical fitness agree on just what components should be represented and assess their relative importance, test scores may be devised to incorporate these factors in the appropriate percentages[10].

[10] Indicates the definitive action required and places the statement in a prominent place—the end.

ASSIGNMENT 3: IMPROVED TEXT

RAPID MICROMETHOD FOR DETECTION AND IDENTIFICATION
OF AMINO ACIDS WITH AUXOTROPHIC BACTERIA[1]

S. Briter

INTRODUCTION

Many[2] authors (2–4) have used autographic methods to detect and identify biologically required molecules (for review see ref. 4). In the auto—

[1] Title is longer, but much more informative. "Bioassay" has been replaced by the actual kinds of assay meant (detection and identification). The kind of molecules assayed (amino acids) is specified. (Although the method may be applicable to other kinds of molecules, this paper deals only with amino acids.) Finally, the *kind* of method (namely, a bacteriological one) is indicated and the intelligent reader immediately recognizes the principle on which it is based (auxotrophic bacteria are mutant bacteria with specific nutrient requirements).

[2] If there are many authors, give them—or examples of them—not just your own name or that of colleagues!

cules by autographic methods. This problem[7] has recently been reviewed (4). These[8] procedures, in which
nutritionally deficient mutant bacteria are suspended in minimal media and show zones of growth
following[9] incubation in the presence of the required nutrilite, are in possession of a multi-
plicity[10] of advantages over the more[11] conventional
bioassay techniques being conducted in liquid media.
These[12] include not only simplicity[13] of technique but
also involve[14] the reduction[5] of interference[5] from
inhibitory materials which may reveal their presence[13] in crude sample extracts as natural constituents, or as inadvertent extraction procedure residues[15] (5), as well as their[16] direct applicability[5]
to paper chromatograms where they may aid in the
identification[5] of spots[17]. Their principal disadvantage, being[18] that samples of relatively[19] high
concentration are required, has been largely com-
pensated for by the incorporation[5] of tetrazolium
salts in the solid[20] bioassay medium. Reduction[5] of
these compounds occurs[14] during growth[5] of the test

[7] What problem? (Rule 2)
[8] Warning word. In this case the author passes the test: antecedent ("autographic
methods") is unambiguous and reasonably close by.
[9] Warning word—ends in "ing." *After* always preferable as a preposition.
[10] Grandiloquence. (Rule 1, Be Simple and Concise)
[11] Necessary? (Rule 2)
[12] Antecedent "techniques" or "advantages"? (Rule 2)
[13] Abstract noun derived from adjective. Be simple. (Rule 1)
[14] Warning word—colorless verb, which can probably be replaced by a vigorous
one. See Table 1 of Chapter 6
[15] String of modifiers (Rule 4, Break Up Noun Clusters and Stacked Modifiers).
As so frequently happens, unraveling the string shows how inappropriate some
of the adjectives are.
[16] Antecedent "residues", "materials"? (Rule 2)
[17] The polysyllabic fog has swallowed up all meaning by this time.
[18] Awkward construction.
[19] Relative to what? (Warning word; Rule 2)
[20] The first we are told about this. Anyway, agar is *not* solid.

graphic procedure, nutritionally deficient mutant
bacteria with specific nutrient requirements are
suspended in an agar medium in a petri dish or on a
glass plate.[3] After incubation with the required
nutrilite they show zones of growth.

The technique has many advantages over conventional bioassays in liquid media. It[4] is simpler;
it is not subject to interference by inhibitors that
occur naturally in crude sample extracts or result
from extraction procedures (3); and it can be used
directly to identify the small amounts of material
contained in spots cut out from paper chromatograms.[5] The main disadvantage, namely that
concentrated samples are required, has been overcome
in one laboratory (3) by the incorporation of
tetrazolium salts in the agar medium. These salts

[3] Specific details are given, to bring the technique vividly before the reader's
eye. These details can all be deduced by your students from later passages in
the Faulty Text.

[4] Warning word, but the antecedent ("technique") is in fact unambiguous. In the
sentence that follows, the expressions have been simplified by the substitution
of verbs for abstract nouns. In addition, the ideas are conveyed in three parallel
sentences. Parallel constructions are easy for the reader to follow, especially
when the writer is giving a list, as here.

[5] Expansion for clarity. The technique was *not* "applied directly to paper
chromatograms," but to spots cut out from paper chromatograms.

bacteria, giving criteria of response[5] the sensitivity of which is greater than with tube assay
(4,5). A method here presented holds promise[5] of
offering a further increase in sensitivity[13] and
economy of time, which may possibly further enhance
the potential[21] usefulness[13] of bioautography methods.

METHODS

The test organism used was a series of auxotrophic
mutants of E. coli, and a strain of Lactobacillus
arabinosus. The organism was first grown in nutrient
broth and cells from log phase cultures[22]
centrifuged[23], followed[24] by washing, and a resuspen-
sion[5] then[23] made[14] in 2X minimal medium. The R medium
(1) was employed[25] for E. coli and pantothenate assay
medium, on the other hand, was used in experiments
involving L. arabinosus. The cell suspension is[26] now
mixed with equal volumes of 3% agar, liquefied and
cooled[27] to 45°C. Adjustment[5] of the suspension is
undertaken[14] so that the density of the seeded agar
approximated 10^5 or 10^6 cells per ml.

The sample of the growth factor being assayed
need not always be the same,[28] in some cases it was a
small section cut from a paper chromatogram, but
in these[29] experiments designed to calibrate the
method it[29] consisted of measured quantities (up to
0.1 ml) of a solution of the growth factor being

[21] "Possibly . . . potential" is redundant and pompous. (Rule 1)
[22] The sort of noun cluster that close examination shows to be inaccurate.
[23] Omitted auxiliary.
[24] Warning word ending in "ed" (especially ambiguous in this context because
   it is preceded by a genuine past participle).
[25] Bombastic variant of "used"; pointless variation of verb within the sentence.
   (Rule 1)
[26] Mixed tenses (see footnote 10, Improved Text).
[27] Ambiguity: was the *mixture* liquefied and cooled, or only the agar?
[28] Incorrect punctuation.
[29] Antecedent?

are reduced if the test bacteria grow, and the
resultant blue color can be detected with a sensitivity greater than in the tube assay.

The technique presented here further increases
the sensitivity of the method and makes it less
time-consuming.[6]

METHODS

The organisms used were a strain of Lactobacillus
arabinosus and a series of auxotrophic mutants of
Escherichia coli.[7] Each organism was grown in
nutrient broth and cells in log-phase growth were
centrifuged, washed, and resuspended in double-
strength[8] minimal medium. For E. coli, R medium (1)
was used; for L. arabinosus, pantothenate assay
medium.[9] The cell suspension was[10] mixed with an
equal volume of 3% aqueous agar that had been
liquefied and cooled to 45 °C. The suspension was
diluted until it contained[11] 10^5-10^6 cells per ml.

The sample of amino acid or other growth factor
being assayed need not always be in solution (for
example, it may be in the form of a spot cut from a
paper chromatogram), but in the calibrating experiments it consisted of measured quantities (up to 0.1
ml) of an aqueous solution. The sample was placed in

---

[6] Note division of the Introduction into three paragraphs: (a) general orientation
and description of autography; (b) advantages and disadvantages of the method
to date; (c) advantages of technique to be described.

[7] Consistency. If *Lactobacillus* is spelled out (as it should be, when first mentioned), *Escherichia* must be, too.

[8] "Double strength" has replaced the laboratory jargon "2 ×."

[9] Notice the conciseness of parallel constructions.

[10] In descriptions of a method recommended for future use, the present tense
may be used and is appropriate if a final "recipe" is being presented. However,
the writer must avoid mixing past and present, and when he is describing not
only the method but also tests of the method (for which the past tense would
be needed) it is best to stick to the past.

[11] Removal of the verb "approximated" and use of Rule 2 showed that "density"
was entirely misused.

analyzed[30]. The sample, whether a drop of a solution, or a section of paper, or a sample of varying[31] nature[32], is then placed in the center of a sterile microscope slide, presterilized[33] in petri dishes, and the inoculum of[10] one drop of seeded agar added. If a liquid sample volume[34] is large, it should be permitted to evaporate first.[35] A warmed, sterile coverslip is then placed immediately over the agar, which flows to the edges of the cover slip and solidifies almost at once. In order to assure[36] spreading of the agar in a thin, uniform layer, prewarming[33] of the slides by incubation or by some other means[10] would appear[37] to be indicated[14]. Due to[38] the tendency of evaporation[5] of agar during subsequent incubation[5], the edges of the coverslip may be sealed to the slide with paraffin, and[39] the slides were[26] incubated at 37 °C. Growth response[5] may be ascertained within a few hours, however[40] slides sealed in this[29] manner may be stored without more than minimal[41] drying of the agar for several days or even weeks after preparation[5], if the investigator so desires.[42]

RESULTS

Response[5] to relatively[19] large concentrations of sample is detectable upon gross macroscopic examina-

---

[30] Meaning of this word? (Rule 2)
[31] Forbid this word except when *continuous* variation is meant.
[32] Woolly word, see Table 1 of Chapter 6 and Gowers.
[33] The fatuous "pre." (Rule 1)
[34] Noun cluster. (Rule 4)
[35] Illogical order of description.
[36] Dangling infinitive. (Rule 2)
[37] Outlaw "would appear" under all circumstances. (Rule 1)
[38] Warning word: "because of" almost always better.
[39] Inappropriate conjunction.
[40] Common misuse for "but." (Rule 1)
[41] Warning word, see Table 1 of Chapter 6.
[42] Pompous verbal flourish. (Rule 1)

the center of a microscope slide (previously steril-
ized in a petri dish), and allowed to evaporate if
its volume was large. The petri dish was warmed
slightly, one drop of seeded agar was added, and a
warmed, sterile coverslip was immediately placed
over the agar, which flowed to the edges of the
coverslip and solidified in a thin, uniform
layer. Because the agar solution tends to evaporate
during subsequent incubation, the edges of the
coverslip were sealed to the slide with paraffin.
The slides were incubated at 37°C. Growth can be
observed within a few hours, but slides sealed with
paraffin can be stored with negligible drying of
the agar for days or weeks if necessary.

RESULTS

With concentrated samples, a positive response is
easily soon: the slide clouds over heavily. Positive

tion[5] of slides after incubation[5] by a heavy
clouding of the agar. Detection[5] of lesser amounts
is possible upon microscopic observation and
examination utilizing a low-power microscope
objective.[43] Formation[5] of well-defined microcolonies, especially in the case[32] of E. coli,
occurs[14] in the presence of very[41] small quantities
of the required nutrilites. Titration[5] of the precise end-point at which no response[5] occurs[14] can be
determined only by careful comparisons of seeded,
unsupplemented minimal agar control slides[15].
Observation[5] of results is possible with coli[44]
after 4 hours of incubation, overnight incubation[5]
was[45] required for the arabinosus[44] assays.

No advantage was derived from the addition[5] of
tetrazolium salts to the agar, which has been
reported (5) to enhance visualization[5] of growth
response. In our hands, formation[5] of microcolonies
occurs[14] well before any appreciable reduction[5] of
the dye is seen.

Table 1 shows a comparison of the absolute
quantities of some amino acids for which detection[5]
is possible by the slide method, versus corresponding results for tetrazolium-containing plates
prepared by another suggested (5) technique. The
slide method would appear[37] to offer higher
sensitivity. The concentration of arginine detectable by slide autography was 0.1 μg, an order of
magnitude[46] greater than by the conventional
technique. The values for histidine and methionine
were 0.05 versus 0.1 and 1.0, respectively, again

---

[43] Phrase from "observation" onwards is verbose: repetition of "microscop-"
warns the alert reviser.

[44] Jargon.

[45] Clash of tense with "is" in earlier part of the sentence. Actually, there are two
main clauses; either the comma should be replaced by a semicolon or a conjunction such as "whereas" should be inserted. (Rule 2)

[46] Grandiloquence: see discussion of Rule 1 in Chapter 6.

response to lower concentrations can be detected
under the low-power microscope. E. coli, especially,
forms well-defined microcolonies with small quantities of nutrilites. The precise concentration at
which there is no longer any response can be determined only by microscopic comparison with control
slides bearing seeded agar solution but no added
nutrilite. Results can be seen with E. coli after 4
hours of incubation, but L. arabinosus needs
incubation overnight.

Addition of tetrazolium salts, which has been
reported (3) to make the growth response more
readily visible, did not improve the method described here; microcolonies formed well before the
dye was reduced to the colored form. Table 1 shows
that, for the four amino acids tested, the present
method is up to 10 times as sensitive as when
tetrazolium salts are added to the test mixture on a
glass plate.

TABLE 1

Detection of amino acids

| Strain | Amount Detectable* | | Amino Acid Requirement |
	Plate autography**	Slide autography***	
E. coli 75	10^{-1}	10^{-2}	tryptophane
E. coli 13	10^{-1}	5×10^{-2}	histidine
E. coli 14	1.0	5×10^{-2}	methionine
E. coli 1875	1.0	10^{-1}	arginine

*   In micrograms
**   With tetrazolium
***   See text

an improvement, and tryptophane yielded once again an order of magnitude[46] of difference in this[29] concentration range.[47]

Using L. arabinosus, detection[5] of about 10^{-3} μg of pantothenic acid was possible utilizing[48] the tetrazolium plate technique, meanwhile[39] detection[5] of 10^{-4} μg and even less was achieved[14] by the slide method advocated here. However E. coli produced a somewhat more satisfactory growth response than L. arabinosus, for this[29] species forms more compact and easily observed microcolonies upon incubation at suitable growth temperatures.[42]

DISCUSSION

It would appear[37] that the slide method will prove more sensitive in most cases[28,32], diffusion[5] is limited to the confines of a single drop of agar and growth response[5] may be observed on a micro level. In addition to the usual advantages of autographic procedures, therefore, the slide method reported

---

[47] Stylistic considerations apart, this sentence is objectionable because it simply repeats what is in the table (see p. 28), but in the wrong order (see p. 120).

[48] Dangling participle (warning word, ends in "ing").

TABLE 1

Sensitivity of detection of amino acids by
autography on microscope slides compared to plate
autography in the presence of tetrazolium salts (5)[a]

Strain of E. coli[b]	Amino acid requirement[c]	Amount detectable	
		Plate Autography	Slide Autography
		μg[d]	
75	Tryptophane	0.1[e]	0.01
13	Histidine	0.1	0.05
14	Methionine	1.0	0.05
1875	Arginine	1.0	0.1

[a] Note specificity of title of the table and its relation to the title of the article.
[b] Repetition of *E. coli* eliminated.
[c] Columns rearranged to logical order.
[d] Units placed within the table instead of in footnotes.
[e] Clumsy and pretentious designations (10^{-1}, etc.) made rapidly comprehensible.

With L. arabinosus, the "tetrazolium plate" technique could detect 10^{-3} μg of pantothenic acid whereas the slide method could detect as little as 10^{-4} μg.
The growth response with this organism was, however,
more difficult to observe than with E. coli, which
forms more compact microcolonies on incubation.

DISCUSSION

Because diffusion on the microscope slide is confined to a single drop of agar, the slide method can
be expected to be both more sensitive and less time-

here appears to offer the possibility[13] of a quicker, more sensitive test. Requiring[48] only negligible amounts of sample, it's[49] performance[5] is possible with a minimum[50] of equipment and supplies.

The slide method reported appears to offer a possible useful application[5] in identification[5] of unknown paper chromatogram spots[51]. Since the lowest concentration of most amino acids detectable as spots lies in the range of 10^- to about 5.0 μg[52] (6) and this method will detect as little as 10^{-2} μg (Table 1), it would perhaps be possible in many cases[32] to cut a spot area into two or more pieces[53] and screen it against several different organisms with varying[31] amino acid requirements. The very high specificity of nutrient requiring mutant bacteria[54] would provide a precise means of identification[5] which may often be[26] applied in circumstances wherein limitations[13] of time or availability[13] of sample are prohibitory[55] to identi- fication[5] of spots by more[11] conventional procedures. Using[48] appropriate mutants of certain bacteria, the identification[5] of many types of compounds would be possible using[48] the slide method. The bacteria employed must of course be aerobic or facultative, limiting[48] it's[29,49] applicability[13] somewhat.

[49] Illiteracy.

[50] Rule 2. What, to be precise, is "a minimum of equipment or supplies"? None at all.

[51] Stacked modifiers (Rule 4). Even after unstacking, what are "unknown spots"? (Rule 2)

[52] Grandiloquence, see Baker. (Rule 1)

[53] Can one cut an area into pieces? (Rule 2)

[54] Germanic stacked modifiers (does the nutrient require the bacteria?). See Rule 4 and Baker.

[55] Verb hidden in clumsy phrase. (Rule 1)

consuming than others so far reported. It requires a
negligible amount of sample and little equipment.

The method may perhaps be applied to the identification of unknown compounds on paper chromatograms; spots cut from such chromatograms could be
incubated with auxotrophic bacteria having highly
specific nutrient requirements. Spots of amino acids
that are detectable with spray reagents contain at
least 0.1-5.0 μg (5), and since the slide method
will detect as little as 0.01 μg (Table 1), a single
spot from a chromatogram could, if necessary, be
divided and tested against several organisms with
different amino acid requirements. This bioassay
would be rapid, sensitive, and specific.

The slide method can be used, of course, only
with aerobic or facultative bacteria, and this
restricts its applicability.

REFERENCES[56]

1. Adams, R. 1946. A synthetic medium. J. Bact.
   30:11–12.
2. Bumpkin, N., and Slobb, W. 1951. Chromatography
   in Molecular Biology. P.N.A.S. 13:385–397.
3. Clodd, A. 1963. Studies on bacterial growth.
   This journal 90:10–15.
4. Ford, M. T., and G. T. Ford. 1965. Bioautography.
   Ann. Reviews Microbiol. 19:100–200.
5. Fazoul, P. 1965. Tetrazolium and autography. Ap.
   Microbiol. 5:18–23.
6. Whizz, G., and O. Gosh. 1959. Paper chromatography. Canadian J. Graphite Res. 75–85.

[56] Apart from errors in styling, these references give examples of inappropriately broad titles. Only that in reference 4 is appropriate, since it is the title of a review article (see the name of the journal). The titles in 2 and 5 would need books to do them justice; those in 1, 3, and 5 are laconic without being succinct. In addition, 4 and 5 are misplaced alphabetically, and 2 has not been cited in the text.

REFERENCES[12]

1. Adams, R. 1946. Synthetic growth medium for aerobic bacteria. J. Bacteriol. 30:11–12.
2. Briter, S. 1963. Nutritional requirements of mutants of E. coli. J. Food Sci. 9:10–15.
3. Fazoul, P. 1965. Tetrazolium salts increase sensitivity of autographic detection of amino acids. Appl. Microbiol. 5:18–23.
4. Ford, M. T., and G. T. Ford. 1965. Bioautography. Annu. Rev. Microbiol. 19:100–200.
5. Whizz, G., and O. Gosh. 1959. Paper chromatography of neutral amino acids. Can. J. Genet. Cytol. 18:75–85.

[12] Improved titles have been provided here for articles in the references. Needless to say, this cannot be done in real life, and you should make your students realize that once they have published an uninformative title, both the situation and the article are essentially irretrievable.

Other changes in the references are: ref. 2 has been deleted, our "Clodd" has become "Briter," a real journal title has replaced "*This journal*," and the first authors are now in correct alphabetical order. Reference 3 has been given a title that is a statement: a refreshing occasional change from the usual form, and one that is often used in good journals (see, for example, *Science*). In reference 5, a real, more likely journal has replaced the unlikely, probably mistaken one in reference 6 of the faulty text; and a volume number has been inserted.

8

The Final Steps

YOU WILL QUOTE:

Trelease, p. 39 ("Choice of Title")
      pp. 42–43 ("Abstracts," points 2–5).

This chapter contains the remaining steps in writing a journal article. You may want, as suggested in Chapter 5, to give your students a "preview" of them before plunging into the detailed consideration of style for which the framework is given in Chapter 6.

STEP 21: *Give Drawings to Illustration Department*

Revision of the text sometimes shows that corresponding changes are needed in the figures, designed at Step 10. It is not wise, therefore, to have drawings made professionally before one is sure of the final form. Now, however, the illustrators should be given as much time as possible to complete their work while the author works on the final steps in writing. Emphasize the importance of consulting the Instructions to Authors and of sending to the illustration department any special requirements of the journal (e.g., type of drawing paper, size of lettering) relating to the drawings to be submitted.

STEP 22: *Write Title and Abstract in Final Form*

You and your students gave a lot of thought to the title and the early form of the abstract (the synopsis), back at Step 5. Why should these parts of the manuscript need revision? Because now a different objective must be considered. The purpose of writing title and synopsis at that early stage, you will remember, was for the author to clarify for himself his aims and intentions. Now he must think of the title and abstract from the reader's point of view. He must check that they accurately reflect the contents of the article as it has emerged after all the modifications we have discussed. He must also ensure that the title, especially, is an effective guide for scientists rapidly scanning lists of titles for information relevant to their interests. Of all the parts of the article, the title will surely enjoy the widest circulation; all the more reason, then, that it should be a fitting and worthy representative of the article's contents.

The title should be long enough to be fully informative, but it should contain no unnecessary words like "On the . . ." and "Studies in . . .". The tersest form of expression is always the most telling; furthermore, automatic indexing systems reject parts of excessively long titles, and may retain insignificant words at the expense of more important ones. Here you have an opportunity, invoking these considerations, to discourage the "serialization" of articles—publication of a series of numbered articles, all under a general title. This practice is objectionable for another reason also: its patent self-advertisement antagonizes rather than informs.

A title should not suggest too much through too broad a generalization (e.g., "Extraction of Proteins from Tissues," when the article deals with the extraction of only *one* class of protein from certain mammalian tissues) or through vagueness ("Some Photosynthetic Reactions"), but neither should it attempt to be an abstract in itself ("Conversion of Tetracyclic Terpenes to Derivatives of Geranyl Geraniol and Some Unidentified Oxidation Products Under the Influence of Broad-Spectrum Light at Temperatures Below 0°C and High Pressures"). Much information *can* be given in a short title, with the aid of a little ingenuity and ruthless suppression of nonessentials ("Light-Induced Conversion of Terpenes to Geranyl Geraniol [at Low Temperatures and High Pressures]" . . . the last six words can be omitted if the main novel achievement was the conversion, whereas they are needed if the conversion was already known under other conditions). See Trelease, p. 39, for further guidance on this matter, and provide good and bad examples from your own reading.

Making an abstract from the finished paper will resemble the assignment at the end of Chapter 3. Refer to Trelease, pp. 42–43, for principles to be followed, and recommend that the spirit of the synopsis written at Step 5 be studied and as far as possible retained—for the abstract will be the reader's first encounter with the paper, and his mind will be as unclouded by familiarity with its contents as was the writer's at that early stage.

Clarify at this point the difference between an abstract and a summary (on this matter, Trelease, p. 42, is at variance with present usage). An abstract must stand alone and be intelligible without reference to the text (especially as it may be reprinted unchanged in a secondary publication, quite divorced from the text). A summary serves only to bring together, for a reader who has already read the paper, the article's salient points; it often gives only conclusions, without indicating the experiments that have led to them or the purpose and significance of the work performed. An abstract therefore appears at the head of an article and a summary at the end. Information specialists nowadays are urging that, of the two, abstracts are far more valuable to many users, and that summaries have had their day.

A further distinction is between indicative and informative abstracts. The former are descriptive and often omit all numerical data, whereas the latter try to give all the results of the paper itself and are often accepted as substitutes for the original paper when it is, for example, in an inaccessible language. Informative abstracts clearly call for great skill and experience on the part of the abstracter and are usually entrusted to professionals. This does not mean, however, that the author's indicative abstract can be a sloppy, amateur affair. The writer must attempt, within the space allowed, to convey the purpose, general experimental design, conclusions, and, if possible, significance of his work—not merely list his results in a dull, meaningless catalogue.

STEP 23: *Reread the Journal's Instructions to Authors Before Having the Manuscript Typed*

In view of all the time and effort expended on organization, content, and style, we have at least the hope that the draft resulting from the revision steps will be the final one, fit for transmission to the journal. Before it is typed, therefore, both the typist *and the author* should reread the Instructions to Authors of the journal to which the article is to be submitted—not, this time, in order to get a general impression of the journal's scope and procedures but to study and apply all the minutiae of convention adopted by the chosen journal. In particular, you could mention the following points to be watched for: position and length of abstract, style of headings and subheadings, paragraphing, numbering (Roman or Arabic?) of tables and figures, layout of tables, authorities given for nomenclature, form of biblio-graphic references, and number of copies to be submitted. You will find it useful to keep a file of Instructions to Authors from several journals to show to your class.

You may or may not care to go into any more detail on these mechani-cal matters, which constitute "publisher's style." Trelease, pp. 52–66, has some useful tips for the uninitiated. The essential point to be made is that these details are not to be dismissed as unimportant fiddle-faddle, beneath the notice of the gifted scientist who is fully occupied with pushing back the frontiers of knowledge. Attention to such matters is a mark of scrupulous care, which cannot fail to make a good impression on editors and reviewers. If your students show a tendency to charge editors and publishers with be-ing too compulsively devoted to points of mechanical consistency, ask them whether they consider it important, in any series of experiments, to make up solutions with chemicals of a consistent grade of purity, or whether they use tap water in one experiment and sterile, triple-distilled water in the next, or whether they think it proper in a paper to give dimensions in inches or meters, fractions or decimals, indiscriminately and whimsically. In my ex-perience, the correlation between excellence of preparation of a manuscript and the chances of its ultimate acceptance is high, because fastidious presentation is a mark not only of good manners but of good training. It is an indication of careful and reliable work in all phases of the investi-gation.

When the manuscript has been typed, it must be proofread (before Step 24) by the author, preferably with the aid of a colleague or assistant who reads aloud from the original while the author notes any corrections on the top copy and simultaneously on each carbon copy.

STEP 24: *Departmental Review*

When the final draft is ready, the author will do well to offer it, before for-mal submission, for informal review to three types of critic, who may be personified as: the man in the same laboratory, the man down the hall, and the author's wife. By the "man in the laboratory" I mean someone inti-mately involved with similar work, who can criticize the methodological details and perhaps suggest alternative interpretations of the results; the ideal adviser here may actually be in another institution, hundreds of miles away. The "man down the hall" represents a fellow scientist who will be able to point out where the text is unintelligible to anyone outside the sub-specialty or limited coterie to whom the paper is primarily addressed. For "wife" one may substitute—in this context only!—any nonscientific friend who cares enough for the author to stumble through the technicalities to discover what seems to be a disjointed sentence, a word with undesirable or risible overtones, an overlong paragraph, an apparent failure in logic, or an awkward transition. These three critics give the author something he is unable to provide for himself: distance. Whether he chooses to take their advice is a matter of judgment based on whom he wants to reach with the article and how he wants to influence his audience. In order to avoid offend-ing these kind advisers, he can ask them to write their suggestions down for him to study, and thank them after due time for reflection. And he should not continue to ask advice indefinitely, or confusion and despair will surely seize him.

STEP 25: *Shelve the Manuscript for a While*

Again in the interests of obtaining distance, the author should put the last draft of the manuscript away for at least a week and then read it critically before submitting it for formal review by the journal. This enables him to look at it with a fresh eye, as though he were a reader coming upon it for the first time (and this is the frame of mind he should aim for).

Now the paper is ready to go. After a final check that the pages are correctly numbered and are all present, together with tables and figures, in all copies, the manuscript can be mailed. Tell your students not to forget the brief covering letter of submittal—which shows (among other things) with whom the editor should correspond and the date the manuscript left the author's desk—or the protective cardboard for the figures, if this seems necessary. Some Instructions to Authors stipulate using registered or certi-fied mail; in any case, the author should, of course, retain at least one com-plete and accurate copy in his files just in case anything should go wrong. Suggest that authors enclose a postcard for the editor to acknowledge the paper's arrival, but warn them not to count on a *decision* in less than six weeks. Sober and thoughtful review can easily take that long, although it sometimes requires much less. A polite letter of inquiry at the end of this time is not out of place. If the postcard acknowledging receipt is not returned it is reasonable to write sooner, because some mail does disappear.

You may encounter occasionally the naive question: "Is it permissible to submit the article to several journals simultaneously?" I need hardly explain how you should answer this: how submission of a manuscript to one journal tacitly implies that it is not under consideration elsewhere, and what cogent reasons there are for avoiding duplicate publication. Most vivid of all is to ask the student what he would do if two journals decided simultaneously to accept the article, and what sort of a reputation this would earn him.

The handling and correction of proof is adequately dealt with in many textbooks, including Trelease and the CBE *Style Manual*, and will not be dealt with here.

Do not be surprised if, at this stage of your course, your students beg you to instruct them in further refinements of style. My experience is that at least some of the young scientists who begin your course with profound indifference to the power of words become intoxicated with the intricacy and subtlety of language. Don't be afraid to let yourself go with these students— set your sights higher with them, and let them glimpse your own conviction that in precision and truth lies also beauty. Tether your instruction firmly to prosaic principles of parallelism, word-order for emphasis, appropriateness of metaphor, and so on; but let your examples range widely across all of literature, from scientific to literary and back again, and allow your students to experience the joy that comes from exactly the right word in precisely the right place. The books by Lucas, Tichy (p. 56), and W. Paul Jones (180) provide excellent material.

9

Responding to the Editor

This part of the course is optional, but I think you will find that your students are extremely interested in what happens to a paper after it reaches the editorial office. If most of them go on to research work as a career they will probably publish several papers and will need to know how to cope with editors' and reviewers' suggestions. This chapter may help them, too, to be systematic as well as sympathetic reviewers themselves when the time comes for them to judge others' work.

Before beginning to talk about corresponding with the editors of journals' you may have to explain that the system of editorial review varies from journal to journal, but almost always involves consideration of the manuscript by at least one expert in the field besides the editor. Description of the systems from your own knowledge and experience will constitute the most vivid possible exposition, so I have not attempted one here.

The editor's letter to the author will contain one of three decisions:

1. *Outright Acceptance.* This decision, the author's dream, is rare. Scientists are, by nature and training, critical, and it is unusual for them to find that anything is perfect, even when they believe that it is important and well executed. For a few journals, however, outright acceptance is routine: for example, the Proceedings of the National Academy of Sciences of the United States and of many other countries. The high standards of these journals are maintained by reason of the caliber of the authors who are permitted to publish in them, namely the members of the Academy. No response to a letter of acceptance is strictly necessary, although a gracious note of thanks cannot be taken amiss.

2. *Outright Rejection.* If the tone of the editor's letter makes it clear that he and his reviewers have fundamental objections to the manuscript and if the letter does not explicitly offer further consideration of the matter, the author is usually well advised to accept the decision with as

much grace as he can muster. According to the reasons for rejection given, he should:

(a) Consider sending the manuscript, suitably modified as to "publisher's style" (see Step 23), to another journal. This course should usually be followed only if the reason given for rejection is that the article is too specialized (or not specialized enough) for the journal first chosen and would be more appropriately published elsewhere. Step 3 (What Is the Most Suitable Journal?) should have obviated this response, but we all make mistakes.

(b) Consider modifying the content and perhaps the length of the article, taking advantage of the criticisms offered, and submit it to another journal. If the experts in charge of the first journal so clearly disliked the manuscript on first submission, they are unlikely to view a modified version with any great relish, but a new editorial board may be more charitable or work within another frame of reference.

(c) Consider withholding the manuscript until he has obtained more extensive data and better support for his conclusions. Steps 1 (What Is the Right Time to Publish?) and 24 (Departmental Review) should have saved the author from this humiliation; but again, he and his friends may easily have underestimated the strictness of reviewers.

(d) Consider contesting the editor's decision. If the author feels that the reviewers have shown incompetence, have misunderstood a major issue, or have been unjust (and since reviewers are human beings, all these things happen), he has every right to urge the editor to reconsider his decision. Letters written in anger—and still worse, telephone calls—have little chance of success. Calm, reasoned rebuttals are almost always considered sympathetically, for editors are rarely complete fools or inflexible tyrants. They are busy, though, so tell your students to keep such rebuttals succinct and to the point. One copy of the manuscript should accompany the letter unless it is clear that the editor still has one in his files. Politeness is always well received.

3. *Request for Revision.* The "decision letter" often contains this request. The author should first determine whether the revisions requested are major or minor and then examine whether the letter states that the article would be *acceptable* if thus revised or only offers *further consideration* by the editorial board. This distinction may decide whether the revisions are worth the trouble.

Above all, the author should realize that the recommended revisions are *suggestions*, generally put forward by responsible scientists anxious only to further science. They are not commands or conditions of acceptance. He must make up his mind whether they will improve his paper or not, and adopt them or not accordingly. Pages on which any changes have been made (beyond a few words inserted or deleted) should be retyped, and the revised manuscript should be returned together with (a) a letter of thanks to the editor and the reviewers for their help; (b) a copy of the original manuscript if this will help the editor; (c) a list of responses to the reviewer's comments, giving reasons for *not* accepting the recommendations where appropriate; and (d) a list of changes made in the manuscript. All these considerate actions will assist *and expedite* the handling of the revised manuscript.

Correspondence concerning publication of a paper is often, unnecessarily, the cause or the product of anger. It should not be. Mature authors are those who have learned to value the constructive criticism of fellow scientists and to appreciate the sacrifice of anything up to 20 hours of time and (unpaid) effort on behalf of an unknown colleague. The young scientist will reach that maturity more quickly if the mechanism of the procedure, and especially the motives of those who participate, are well explained at an early stage of his career. Any sensible person will concede that it is preferable to receive criticism in private, before the publication of his paper, than after, when it has entered the public forum.

Above all, discourage your students from guessing at the reviewers' identities. Editors agree that such guesses are—surprisingly, perhaps—usually wrong. If the review is unfavorable, this inevitably leads to completely unfounded antagonism. The best approach may be to believe that every review is written by God; if this seems impossible or unlikely, tell your class to imagine its author to be a highly intelligent, though fallible, archangel whom they are unlikely ever to encounter in real life.

RELATED TOPICS

10

Design of Tables and Figures

You should read:

Trelease, Chapters 4 and 5; pp. 25–29.

CBE *Style Manual* (2nd ed.); pp. 50–58.

The following books go into the subject more deeply, and are useful for background information, further study, or special courses:

Tables: Zeisel, Hans. *Say It With Figures*. 1957. 4th revised edition. Harper and Row, New York; Routledge and Kegan Paul, London (1958).

Statistics: Worthing, A. G., and J. Geffner. 1943. *Treatment of Experimental Data*. John Wiley and Sons, New York; Chapman and Hall, London.

Graphs: American Standards Association. 1959. *Illustrations for Publication and Projection* (Bull. Y 15.1-1959). American Standards Association, New York.

Timing:

1 to 2 hours, depending on the degree of detail you employ. The discussion will be more meaningful if your students have already designed tables and figures for a journal article or for the major assignment in Part 1 of this book.

GENERAL PRINCIPLES

Tables and figures often constitute the entire evidence put forward in an article to support the author's conclusions. It is vital, therefore, that they be carefully planned. The planning should begin very early in the writing of the article (see Chapter 3, Step 10), both for the author's sake and for the reader's.

You should distinguish clearly here between "private" and "public" purposes in constructing tables and graphs. The private purposes are for clarifying the author's own thinking, and the kinds of table and graph that this activity leads to have usually been roughed out before the author has taken any steps at all toward writing the article. Mostly, therefore, you will be concerned with public purposes—communication of information—although here and there you can interject some useful extensions of the usual techniques of tabulating and graphing for private purposes that will probably be new to your class.

Ideally, each final table or figure should be a single unit of communication, completely informative in itself. Naturally, it will be integrated with the text, but you should get your students to write the text around the evidence instead of composing the text and appending the evidence to it. If each table or figure is designed—and redesigned—to yield the maximum amount of information before any part of the text is begun, the latter will need a minimum of words and the paper will thereby gain in clarity.

Like prose, tables and figures convey their message clearly only if their purpose is exactly defined. The student must ask himself "What is this table or figure supposed to do?"—and train himself *not* to answer merely "Show the data"! Purposeless tabulation, like purposeless writing, can lead to only one end: mystification. The data must be shown *meaningfully*. Tables and graphs are supposed to accomplish something: to reveal comparisons or changes and, if possible, to indicate why they are significant.

In general, one can say that the objectives of these nontextual parts of a paper are as follows:

1. Tables and figures (with, of course, their ancillary titles, legends, and footnotes) should describe an experiment and its purpose (of course, in a highly abbreviated way), besides showing its results.
2. Tables, in addition to (1), should present accurate numbers for comparison with work described in other papers.
3. Figures, in addition to (1), should reveal trends and relationships (graphs) or record natural appearances (light and electron micrographs).

Sometimes these objectives overlap: tables can reveal trends and relationships, if well designed, and under certain conditions graphs can present precise values. Sometimes all the objectives cannot, for practical reasons, be achieved, but this does not absolve the writer from the obligation to make a strenuous attempt to achieve them, before he can be satisfied with the design of his illustrative material.

An author frequently has to choose between tabular and graphical presentation of the data. Teach your students to make the choice by reference to the purpose: are shapes and trends more important to the readers, or exact values? If the experiments were repeated, would one expect only qualitatively similar results or should they be quantitatively the same? Rarely, both vivid presentation and precise numbers will seem important. The author then has the considerable task of convincing the editor that his reasons for presenting data in both forms are compelling. Above all, the author should not alternate tables and figures or choose between them arbitrarily merely because he wants variety. If he does so, the reader will find himself wondering "Why are these results in a histogram, those in a line graph, those in a table?" and will be distracted from the main business of understanding the purport of the paper.

The last general principle to convey is that undue complexity in tables and figures must be avoided. If this principle is followed, each table and figure reveals purpose and results at a glance. To gain practice in applying the principle, the student should first draw up his data in such a way that each table or figure makes only one point, and leads to a single conclusion. This may produce an uncomfortable proliferation of illustrative material and an undesirable repetition of data. But the resultant single-conclusion, sharply focused tables and figures, even though they are too numerous to be used in this form, will almost certainly suggest the most effective way of showing the results. All that then remains is for the author to combine the illustrations and eliminate redundant or irrelevant material, using the criterion that each item must contribute to the over-all purpose of the table. Note that a *negative* contribution to purpose also justifies an item's inclusion: your students are not to run happily away with the criterion as an excuse for the suppression of results that don't quite fit!

TABLES

List the Titles of All Tables and Check their Intelligibility and Relationships to One Another

As with planning the entire article, the planning of tables profits enormously if the title is well thought out at the start. The title announces the purpose of the table. It can, in addition, indicate the experimental design— but usually not the methods, which belong in the footnotes. Title, footnotes, and column headings together make up the description of the table and should form a complete unit that is independent of the text.

Encourage your students to think of the tables for any one article as a coherent series and to list *all* their titles on a separate sheet. They could produce something like this:

Table 1.   Time course of hydrolysis of glyceryl 1-monoacetate by rat liver mitochondria.

Table 2.   Effect of suspending medium on hydrolysis of 3-acetoxypropane-1, 2-diol as measured by UV absorption.

Table 3.   Effect on monoacetin hydrolysis of activators and inhibitors.

Table 4.   Effect of substrate concentration on hydrolysis by rat liver mito-chondria of 1-monoacetin.

As soon as the list is made it is clear that some redundancies and inconsistencies can be eliminated.

(a) *Redundancy.*   The phrase "by rat liver mitochondria" is needed in title 1; if all the other tables also refer to rat liver mitochondria, the phrase can be omitted thereafter, and should not be allowed to creep back into title 4. Similarly, does the sudden appearance in title 2 of "as measured by UV absorption" mean that this was *not* the method used for Table 1? The UV measurement, being experimental method, should be relegated to the footnotes unless it is of cardinal importance.

(b) *Inconsistency.*   Title 3 is in itself ambiguous (activators and inhibitors are apparently being hydrolyzed instead of the substrate) and also violates two useful rules: allow no purposeless variation of word-order, and place the special point of interest of the table at or near the beginning of the title. And in titles 1–4 four different near-synonyms are used to refer to the same substrate.

The title of the first table is often the place to give the reader most of the necessary orienting information. For example, the animal species used throughout should be mentioned there and can be omitted from later tables; the treatment of different groups of animals can be characterized there even if later they are referred to by letters or numbers; the systematic name of a compound can be given there whereas an abbreviation or trivial name may be more convenient subsequently; and so on. If the tables are considered as a set, the "written material" around each of them is easier to plan and design.

The corrected titles would then read:

Table 1. Time course of hydrolysis of 1-monoacetin by rat liver mito-chondria.

Table 2. Effect of suspension medium.

Table 3. Effect of activators and inhibitors.
Table 4. Effect of substrate concentration.

Study the Format Used by the Journal

Most journals have a standard format for their tables; this format should play a decisive part in an author's planning. Impress upon your students, therefore, the need to obtain a copy of the journal they have chosen to publish in and the importance of keeping that copy before them as they work. Show them typical examples of journals in which horizontal rules only are allowed, or in which vertical rules also may be used; conventions for designating column headings and subheadings and for the placing of units of measure; a journal's insistence on or preference for a heading rather than no heading for the extreme left-hand column; and different symbols for referring to footnotes. Remind them that there is only one thing a secretary complains about more than typing a table: retyping it. The author must master the simple mechanics of table construction before demonstrating his logical prowess in the next steps.

Group Items Logically

Nothing is more irritating for a reader than to have to run his eye back and forth comparing two columns or rows of figures that are not adjacent. A useful rule of thumb is to give the "control" or "normal" values first, either in a column toward the left of the table or in the top row of figures. The writer thereby establishes a "base line" in the table in relation to which other values can be considered. If there is a natural gradation of the numbers, from small to large, which can be stressed without placing the headings of rows or columns in any unnatural order, so much the better. But this consideration should be subject to others. For instance, if a pattern is set up in the first table that is also appropriate for later tables, the reader is grateful if the pattern is not arbitrarily broken.

When a table has been given a logical structure, the text that describes that table should follow the same structure. Have your students criticize Table 1 and its corresponding text:

EXAMPLE OF INCONSISTENCIES BETWEEN TABLE AND TEXT

TABLE 1   *Storage of Brobdingnaldehyde*

Storage Conditions	Days		
	2	7	14
	% remaining		
Corked container (23 °C)	100	43	7
Under nitrogen (0 °C)	100	100	98
In vacuo (23 °C)	100	100	100

Table 1 shows that brobdingnaldehyde stored under vacuum at room temperature showed no decomposition in 2 weeks. The sample stored under nitrogen with refrigeration also showed very little alteration, but less than 10% of the sample stored in air at room temperature remained after 2 weeks.

The reader is automatically disoriented by the author's description of the three conditions of storage, which is in the reverse order from their appearance in the table. (The difficulty of finding relevant data in the table is compounded by the author's taste for elegant variation, so that he refers to "under vacuum" instead of "in vacuo," "room temperature" instead of "at 23 °C," "2 weeks" instead of "14 days," "with refrigeration" instead of "at 0 °C," "less than 10%" instead of "only 7%," and a "corked container" [in the table] instead of "in air".)

Choose the Shape

Again with the journal before him, and with rough sketches of the logical requirements of the tables nearby, the student should consider what different possible shapes are open to him. A journal with a two-column format will generally try to fit the smaller tables into the width of one column. The author should try to cooperate with the journal in designing narrow tables—for the less room tables take, the more chance they stand of being printed close to the corresponding text. Conversely, a journal with small pages handles wide tables best—but the number of columns in the table still cannot be increased without limit, or the type will have to become illegibly small.

Although shape plays a comparatively small role in the design of tables, get your students into the habit of experimenting with shape. When the table is a two-dimensional one, it can always simply be rotated through 90°, and the simple experiment of trying this will often yield a table of more pleasing appearance and one in which fewer words need to be broken to fit into their allotted spaces. Tables of three and more dimensions take more manipulation—which means only that the experiment is more interesting.

Column Headings and Footnotes

As you have already pointed out, the title, column headings, and footnotes (together with the entries in the first left-hand column) must form a harmonious and complete whole. Division of material between column headings and footnotes is dictated by the need for extreme brevity in the former; the task of choosing words of great pith and moment with a limited number of letters recalls the problem of writing a thought-provoking abstract with the minimum of words. In general, the footnotes do the legwork for a table and supplement the title and other entries when more details are required.

Condensation

Train your students to recognize that not all the numbers they have determined are sacred. Encourage them to be ruthless in eliminating from each table every value that is inessential to its purpose. Tell them about the American Society for Information Science (formerly American Documentation Institute) in Washington, D.C., where large compilations of data can be deposited, on the recommendation of a journal editor, for recall by those few readers of the condensed table who are interested in more details.

Besides dropping actual values from the table, authors can economize on space by eliminating repetitions of words and even reference values, and transferring them to column headings or footnotes as appropriate. In the following example, shown as Tables 2 and 3, the word "Lilliputamine" and the column headed "Glucose" are cases in point. Correction of this table could form a simple assignment.

EXAMPLE OF POOR TITLE, ILLOGICAL GROUPING, AND
UNNECESSARY REPETITION

TABLE 2   *Carbohydrate Composition of Isolated Lilliputamine Hexosides**

Swift's Disease	Glucose	Galactose	Galactosamine
Lilliputamine monohexoside	1.00	0.54	—
Lilliputamine dihexoside	1.00	1.07	—
Lilliputamine trihexoside	1.00	0.96	1.17
Lilliputamine tetrahexoside	1.00	1.83	1.19
Gulliver's Disease			
Lilliputamine monohexoside	1.00	0.78	—
Lilliputamine dihexoside	1.00	1.03	—
Lilliputamine trihexoside	1.00	1.24	1.18
Lilliputamine tetrahexoside	1.00	2.03	1.07

*Expressed as the molar ratio with glucose as 1.00.

In the improved version of Table 2, given as Table 3, note the change of title, the transfer of footnote material to column heading, the transfer of "Swift's disease" to a logically consistent position, and the elimination of the repeated "Lilliputamine" and "1.00." If an extremely narrow table were desired, even the repeated "hexoside" terminations could be removed. Note also the clarification of the ambiguous dashes in the last column.

A further improvement is shown as Table 4, in which the title brings out the *purpose* of the table; in addition, the values that are to be compared have been put in adjacent columns.

Presentation of Statistics

There is not space here to give a thorough treatment of the presentation of statistical analyses. There are several good textbooks available if you wish to go deeply into the subject (see Trelease, pp. 27–28). The essential point to convey is this: the author is under an obligation to present enough data to enable an interested reader to regenerate the author's raw data, or at least a population of values with the same statistical characteristics.

Your students will probably want to know why: after all, the reader is not invited to check the author's arithmetic or verify figures recorded in laboratory notebooks! So why can't he accept the statistical analysis as

IMPROVED VERSION OF TABLE 2

TABLE 3   *Carbohydrate Composition of Lilliputamine Hexosides Isolated from Human Spleen*

| Lilliputamine Hexoside | Molar Proportion (Glucose = 1.00) | |
	Galactose	Galactosamine
Swift's Disease		
Monohexoside	0.54	—*
Dihexoside	1.07	—*
Trihexoside	0.96	1.17
Tetrahexoside	1.83	1.19
Gulliver's Disease		
Monohexoside	0.78	—*
Dihexoside	1.03	—*
Trihexoside	1.24	1.18
Tetrahexoside	2.03	1.07

* Not detectable (ratio therefore <0.05).

FURTHER IMPROVEMENT OF TABLE 2

TABLE 4   *Similarity of Lilliputamine Hexosides from Spleen in Swift's and Gulliver's Diseases*

Lilliputamine Hexoside	Swift's Disease	Gulliver's Disease
	*molar proportion**	
Galactose		
Monohexoside	0.54	0.78
Dihexoside	1.07	1.03
Trihexoside	0.96	1.24
Tetrahexoside	1.83	2.03
Galactosamine		
Monohexoside	—†	—†
Dihexoside	—†	—†
Trihexoside	1.17	1.18
Tetrahexoside	1.19	1.07

* Relative to glucose = 1.00.
† Not detectable (ratio therefore <0.05).

competent and valid? Assure them that the reader does; but if he is given, in effect, *all* the data (which can be done concisely in the neat summary that statistical methods provide) he can not only repeat the analysis and come to the same result, but perhaps go further, applying other tests and methods, to achieve other or subtler correlations that the writer, perhaps, was not interested in. The process is analogous to giving full experimental details in the Methods section. The reader does not doubt that the experiments were done as described; but we all believe in the principle that another worker should be able to repeat the experiments and obtain the same results, and we therefore provide the means for him to do so. And we all know, both instinctively and from experience, that the worker who does repeat the experiments will—if all goes well—not only get the same results but find something else out, too.

How much information must be provided to satisfy these requirements? Very little more than is customarily provided. As a minimum, your students should learn not only to state the type of test of significance they have applied and the P values obtained (this they are always ready to do), but also to provide standard deviations or standard errors of the means that are being compared, indicate whether the values are SD or SEM, *and specify the number of observations*. Somewhere in our basic training we fail to learn the crucial fact that a standard deviation is useless without n! Beyond this minimum, it is highly desirable to state how the writer established that the data had a normal distribution or were otherwise suitable for the statistical test performed.

My advice is to teach statistics and biometrics, if you wish, in a separate course and to restrict yourself, in the present course, to the few basic precepts that are relevant to the *presentation* of statistics such as have been given here.

Tables with Several Simultaneous Faults

My last example of poor table construction provides a grossly overstocked pair of tables (Tables 5 and 6) that can be reduced to one succinct table (Table 7) by logical consideration of what the author intends to show. Tables 5 and 6 display the data in the order in which they were gathered, which is comfortable for the author but not for the reader. Each table shows fatty acid compositions of classes of lipid—lymph lipids in Table 5 and serum lipids in Table 6. Each table has 12 columns: four classes of lipid (for the moment take the abbreviations CE, TG, FFA, PL as arbitrary designations) from each of three groups of animals. Group C is the control group; the animals in groups A and B have been handled very similarly and really constitute two subgroups of the treated animals.

The conclusion the author wishes to be drawn from the two tables is as follows. In the control animals, the fatty acid compositions of CE in serum and lymph are different, whereas in the treated groups these compositions are similar; therefore, the treatment induces some kind of "leakage" from lymph to serum. The same is true for TG, but for FFA and PL the fatty acid compositions are similar in serum and lymph of the control group anyway, and the treatment does not change the situation.

Clearly, no one is going to compare the appropriate columns in order to reach this conclusion without laborious guidance. This guidance is unnecessary if the data are rearranged so that columns to be compared are adjacent. This has been done in Table 7, where a rapid glance at the top block ("Cholesteryl esters") shows that the first two data columns differ whereas columns 3 and 4 are similar, as are 5 and 6. Thus the data have been *logically grouped*, with the control values placed on the left. The columns have *intelligible headings* and the arbitrary "group" designations (which may be convenient in referring to the groups in the text) have been banished to a footnote. The *shape* of the table has been changed to fit a narrow column. Abbreviations CE, TG, etc. have been eliminated. The *title* is informative: it emphasizes the comparison of lymph with serum lipids; it names the species and the treatment; it gives the effect of the treatment and therefore reveals the underlying purpose of the experiment; it even conveys the crucial result. The comparatively unimportant experimental technique (gas–liquid chromatography) has been placed in a footnote.

In addition, of course, several values have been dropped altogether to produce this extreme condensation. The justification is as follows. *For the purpose of this experiment*, the major fatty acids suffice to make the point. Minor fatty acids neither support nor deny the conclusions—the error of measurement makes all differences between them insignificant. The author may feel "Somebody will want to know the concentration of 17:0 fatty acid in free fatty acids of lymph lipids of the rabbit some day; I have determined it; the value should not be wasted." I think he is deluding himself— but if he feels strongly enough, he should request the editor of the journal

TABLE 5   *Fatty Acid Composition of Lymph Lipids from Thoracic Duct and Hepatic Duct of Group A, B, and C Animals Analyzed by Gas–Liquid Chromatography*

Fatty acids*	Group A (6)†				Group B (5)				Group C (7)			
	CE‡	TG	FFA	PL	CE	TG	FFA	PL	CE	TG	FFA	PL
						%						
12:0	tr.	tr.	tr.	tr.	tr.	tr.	tr.	tr.	tr.	tr.	tr.	tr.
14:0	0.4 ± 0.3§	1.4	2.4	0.3	0.4	2.6	1.1	0.3	0.5 ± 0.3	1.2	1.6	0.4
15:0	1.2 ± 0.7	2.5	1.2	0.5	0.5	0.8	tr.	0.4	0.5 ± 0.3	1.6	0.8	0.4
16:0	17.4 ± 1.7	32.2	27.1	25.9	21.1	38.4	36.5	24.2	31.2 ± 1.4	30.0	30.6	19.4
16:1	4.0 ± 1.3	3.4	4.7	1.0	2.7	2.8	3.5	0.9	5.9 ± 1.0	3.9	4.4	1.6
17:0	1.7 ± 0.8	2.1	2.4	1.5	0.9	1.5	1.2	1.4	2.4 ± 0.9	1.8	1.2	0.8
18:0	6.6 ± 0.9	10.1	5.9	20.3	7.3	8.0	11.8	22.4	10.2 ± 0.2	11.4	7.5	22.6
18:1	30.2 ± 1.7	21.2	16.5	13.8	23.8	20.9	18.8	11.4	18.5 ± 0.8	16.7	20.6	11.3
18:2	27.7 ± 1.5	18.7	20.0	27.6	33.1	18.2	16.5	28.5	22.4 ± 0.8	26.2	19.8	29.8
18:3	7.4 ± 0.7	6.4	14.1	2.4	6.1	5.8	5.9	2.7	4.4 ± 1.3	5.4	8.3	4.5
?	0.4 ± 0.3	0.6	tr.	0.2	1.6	0.6	tr.	0.2	0.5 ± 0.3	0.1	0.4	tr.
?	—	—	—	0.5	0.4	tr.	tr.	0.7	0.5 ± 0.4	0.1	0.4	0.4
20:4	0.9 ± 0.1	tr.	2.4	4.8	1.4	0.3	1.2	6.3	0.5 ± 0.1	0.3	0.4	3.6
?	—	0.2	—	0.2	0.5	—	2.4	0.4	2.0 ± 0.5	0.3	3.6	4.0
?	1.2 ± 0.3	0.4	2.4	0.7	—	—	1.1	tr.	0.5 ± 0.4	tr.	0.4	0.8
Others	0.9 ± 0.6	0.8	1.1	0.3	0.2	0.1	—	0.2	tr.	1.0	tr.	0.4

* Fatty acids designated by chain length:no. of double bonds.

† Group A: cirrhotic, thoracic duct lymph sampled. Group B: cirrhotic, hepatic duct lymph sampled. Group C: control. Number of animals in parentheses.

‡ Cholesteryl esters (CE), triglycerides (TG), free fatty acids (FFA), and phospholipids (PL).

§ Mean ± SEM. tr., < 0.1%.

TABLE 6   *Fatty Acid Composition of Serum Lipids of Group A, B, and C Animals Analyzed by Gas–Liquid Chromatography*

Fatty acids*	Group A (6)†				Group B (5)				Group C(7)			
	CE‡	TG	FFA	PL	CE	TG	FFA	PL	CE	TG	FFA	PL
						%						
12:0	tr.	tr.	tr.	tr.	tr.	tr.	tr.	tr.	—	tr.	tr.	tr.
14:0	0.6 ± 0.4§	1.6	1.9	0.2	0.6	2.0	2.8	0.3	0.6 ± 0.3	1.7	1.4	0.5
15:0	0.6 ± 0.3	1.0	2.0	0.6	0.5	0.8	1.4	0.6	tr.	0.6	0.7	0.4
16:0	19.8 ± 1.0	34.4	30.2	22.8	22.2	38.6	31.9	24.7	18.0 ± 0.7	40.4	34.0	20.5
16:1	4.0 ± 0.7	4.0	3.8	0.9	3.3	3.1	2.8	1.0	3.6 ± 1.0	5.0	4.9	1.3
17:0	1.6 ± 0.4	1.5	0.9	1.4	1.0	1.5	1.4	1.2	0.6 ± 0.5	1.1	0.7	0.8
18:0	5.9 ± 0.2	6.4	9.4	20.5	7.5	6.6	8.3	20.7	6.0 ± 1.4	4.4	8.3	25.9
18:1	28.9 ± 1.0	22.0	19.8	14.6	23.1	19.7	18.1	12.2	18.5 ± 1.9	22.7	21.5	9.2
18:2	26.0 ± 2.4	18.8	14.1	28.5	32.2	20.4	19.4	29.0	40.7 ± 3.4	17.7	17.4	29.7
18:3	6.7 ± 0.6	7.2	9.4	2.8	6.4	6.3	8.3	3.0	4.2 ± 1.2	5.5	9.0	2.5
?	1.0 ± 0.5	0.3	1.9	0.8	0.8	0.5	1.4	0.4	0.6 ± 0.4	0.3	tr.	tr.
?	0.8 ± 0.7	0.2	tr.	0.8	0.3	0.2	tr.	0.9	tr.	0.2	tr.	0.4
20:4	1.1 ± 0.4	0.5	1.9	5.0	1.6	0.3	1.4	5.6	2.4 ± 0.3	—	0.7	6.3
?	0.8 ± 0.4	—	tr.	tr.	0.3	—	2.8	0.2	1.8 ± 0.6	tr.	1.4	2.1
?	0.8 ± 0.6	1.5	3.8	0.8	—	—	—	—	0.6 ± 0.2	0.2	tr.	0.4
Others	0.5 ± 0.4	0.6	0.9	0.3	0.2	—	tr.	0.2	2.4 ± 0.5	0.2	tr.	tr.

For footnotes see Table 5.

TABLE 7 *Similarity in Percentages of Major Fatty Acids from Lipids of Lymph and Serum of Rabbits Made Cirrhotic by Carbon Tetrachloride Treatment*

| Fatty Acid | Controls* | | CCl₄-treated (Cirrhotic)† | | | |
	Thoracic Lymph	Serum	Thoracic Lymph	Serum	Hepatic Lymph	Serum
			Cholesteryl esters			
16:0	31.2 ± 1.4	18.0 ± 0.7	17.4	19.8	21.1	22.2
16:1	5.9 ± 1.0	3.6 ± 1.0	4.0	4.0	2.7	3.3
18:0	10.2 ± 0.2	6.0 ± 1.4	6.6	5.9	7.3	7.5
18:1	18.5 ± 0.8	18.5 ± 1.9	20.2	28.9	23.8	23.1
18:2	22.4 ± 0.8	40.7 ± 3.4	27.7	26.0	33.1	32.2
18:3	4.4 ± 1.3	4.2 ± 1.2	7.4	6.7	6.1	6.4
20:4	0.5 ± 0.1	2.4 ± 0.3	0.9	1.1	1.4	1.6
			Triglycerides			
16:0	30.0	40.4	32.2	34.4	38.4	38.6
16:1	3.9	5.0	3.4	4.0	2.8	3.1
18:0	11.4	4.4	10.1	6.4	8.0	6.6
18:1	16.7	22.7	21.2	22.0	20.9	19.7
18:2	26.2	17.7	18.7	18.8	18.2	20.4
18:3	5.4	5.5	6.4	7.2	5.8	6.3
20:4	0.3	0.0	<0.1	0.5	0.3	0.3
			Free fatty acids			
16:0	30.6	34.0	27.1	30.2	36.5	31.9
16:1	4.4	4.9	4.7	3.8	3.5	2.8
18:0	7.5	8.3	5.9	9.4	11.8	8.3
18:1	20.6	21.5	16.5	19.8	18.8	18.1
18:2	19.8	17.4	20.0	14.1	11.5	19.4
18:3	8.3	9.0	14.1	9.4	5.9	8.3
20:4	0.4	0.7	2.4	1.9	1.2	1.4
			Phospholipids			
16:0	19.4	20.5	25.9	22.8	24.2	24.7
16:1	1.6	1.3	1.0	0.9	0.9	1.0
18:0	22.6	25.9	20.3	20.5	22.4	20.7
18:1	11.3	9.2	13.8	14.6	11.4	12.2
18:2	29.8	29.7	27.6	28.5	28.5	29.0
18:3	4.5	2.5	2.4	2.8	2.7	3.0
20:4	3.6	6.3	4.8	5.0	6.3	5.6

Fatty acids are designated by chain length:no. of double bonds. Percentages were determined by gas–liquid chromatography. SEM values were obtained for all mean values shown, but since they were all closely similar to those in columns 1 and 2, they are not displayed.
* Group C. Number of animals (n) = 7.
† Group A (thoracic, n = 6) and Group B (hepatic, n = 5)

to deposit these data with the American Society for Information Science and not clutter up his table by including them.

Finally, how many statistical data should be given in such an instance? Those shown in Table 7 represent the absolute minimum; other authors might be inclined to add standard errors for all mean values. But if the author points out that all percentages were obtained by the same technique, those given in Table 7 are enough to show that the differences between the first two data columns are going to be highly significant, while those between the other columns are not—which is the whole point of the table. Thus the completeness I advocated in the above section on *Statistics* must, like all principles in writing, be subjected to considerations of common sense, one of the most valuable attributes you can possibly develop in your students.

FIGURES

Figures fall into two distinct categories: those in which numerical data have been transformed into graphs, and those which actually present primary evidence of the scientific observations reported. The second category includes instrumental tracings (e.g., the various kinds of spectra); photographs of (for example) organisms, thin-layer chromatographic plates, or paper electrophoresis strips; and light- or electron micrographs. Your discipline may require still other types, such as maps and charts. Distinguish between the categories, but point out that all figures have two things in common: they all have legends, written by the author, and they all have a shape, determined by the author.

Legends, so often hurriedly tacked onto the manuscript at the very end, form a vital part of the figure and can be a potent force in the article. They consist of a *title*, which orients the reader toward the interpretation and meaning of the figure, followed by an *explanation* of symbols and images within the figure so that it can be intelligently examined, and in many instances *experimental details* about how the figure was obtained. Thus, the figure, with its legend, is a complete unit of communication, just as a table with its accompanying material is.

On the subject of the shape of figures, point out that the shape of graphs can be determined almost arbitrarily by appropriate choice of scale. Hence, as soon as the student begins to design his graphs he should consider the format of the journal he has selected and how the graphs can best be fitted into one or more of its columns. Photographs of instruments or objects may not be so elastic, but often a thoughtful selection of the critical portion of the field of view will prevent disastrous reduction of the whole when the article is printed.

Now go on to consider each type of figure separately. If you want more material than is given below, see the CBE *Style Manual*, pp. 50–55 of the 2nd edition.

Graphs

PURPOSE

When he is planning his graphs, as in all steps in the preparation of a manuscript, the writer must be acutely aware of the *purpose* of what he is doing. In general, the graphing of data that could otherwise appear in a table is justified only when the more vivid display of those data leads to a faster comparison of relationships between them. Thus the purpose of graphs is to promote understanding of the results and to suggest interpretations of their meaning.

FORM

Several possible forms exist, but the most useful ones in scientific work are the plotted curve and the histogram. The data points on which the curve is based must, of course, be shown; refer your students to standard texts (e.g., CBE *Style Manual*, p. 54 of 2nd ed.) for the preferred symbols. Stress the important principle that one must never extrapolate a line or curve outside the points observed without making the reader fully aware of the extrapolation and its inherent dangers. This should lead the student to consider whether it is even appropriate to draw a curve *between* the observed values or whether the histogram representation, with no continuum implied, is the more appropriate form to use. Considerations like this, which stimulate your students to think, are much more valuable to them in the end than detailed discussion of different techniques of graph-making, which will probably be handled by the technical illustrators anyway.

CLARITY

Tell your students to spare no effort in making the graph as clear as possible. Although published graphs can be more complex than is allowable for slides designed for a talk (see Chapter 13), there is a limit to the number of trends and relationships that can be conveyed by any one graph, and you should train your students to recognize this limitation. Again in the interests of clarity, *axes must be labeled*—intelligibly yet compactly, and complete with the units of measure. A little thought will give the units that will require the least number of digits along the axes. Finally, all extraneous background material must be eliminated. For practical help on the technical side, refer your students to the American Standards Association *Illustrations for Publication and Projection.*

TRUTH

Although a pleasing appearance in a graph is a worthy aim, emphasize that students must never sacrifice scientific truth to esthetic appeal. Reiterate the point about unjustified extrapolation. Illustrate the possibility that a choice of scale to achieve a certain over-all shape may falsify the impression of the results. Encourage all students to show not merely mean values but vertical bars for SD or SEM in their graphs, and to make clear in the legend whether SD or SEM is represented and what is the value of n. See whether they can devise some graphical method of distinguishing between a series of values obtained for a single experimental animal subjected to several samplings after treatment and values from different animals sampled independently. There is no standard method for doing this, but thinking about the problem may develop their ability to devise principles of graph-making for themselves.

Instrumental Tracings

Is it essential for the reader that he actually see the trace provided by an automatically actuated pen on a recording chart? How necessary is it to present the UV, IR, or NMR spectrum, the densitometric tracing or the fluctuating concentration of a chromatographic effluent? These are the questions that the author must ask before he plans to present such tracings as figures. Too often, it seems, an author rather thoughtlessly decides to include this kind of evidence, merely because it is something tangible, when a line or two of text would give exactly the same information far more economically.

Get your students into the habit, therefore, of asking these questions, and elicit from them some general principles about the answers they are likely to give. UV spectra, for example, are rarely complex enough to justify reproduction. The same goes for any curve consisting of a single peak of unremarkable shape or several widely spread peaks whose relative height and position can be unequivocally specified in writing. When IR or NMR spectra are used merely to identify a compound by comparison with published spectra, and the curves are indeed identical, the new one need not be published. After all, the reader accepts the author's word on a melting point or optical rotation, observation of which cannot be reproduced in the pages of a journal—so why should he expect proof of a simple statement about the spectrum, just because the technique affords a visual trace?

An instrumental tracing should be shown, however, if

(a) it relates to a new compound;
(b) it is open to several interpretations;
(c) several parts of it remain unexplained or unidentified;
(d) the article describes an instrument or technique of which the tracing is the product;
(e) the shapes of peaks are to be analyzed mathematically or compared with a theoretical shape.

Clearly, the decision about any particular tracing has to be made on its own merits, but you will find that your students are capable of making such decisions quite well, without detailed guidance. Once they learn to ask "Is this tracing really necessary?" common sense will do the rest.

Half-tones

The same questions should arise here as for instrumental tracings: will a figure based on this photograph add something vital to the information offered? In addition, however, the author must be aware that clarity comparable with that in a tracing can be achieved for a half-tone only at considerably increased trouble and expense. Schlieren traces are a case in point. They are often reproduced as evidence of purity (assessed by ultracentrifugation) when a statement would suffice; very gloomy they look, and furthermore often undecipherable, except in broad outline.

On the other hand, a photograph of a thin-layer chromatographic plate or a paper electrophoresis strip often does provide more information than a statement about *RF* values or relative mobilities of the major components, and the information is of a kind difficult to put succinctly into words: the shape of spots, degree of overlap, etc. Although publication of such half-tones can therefore be valuable, the writer should not regard it as obligatory.

When new apparatus is being described, photographs of it are often provided. Here, train your students to ask themselves whether a diagram would not actually be more illuminating. If the half-tone really has some advantage over a drawing (which is rare), advise them always to consult a technical illustrator before taking the photograph or arranging for it to be taken.

Micrographs

Most students know—because of their delight in esoteric knowledge—that electron micrographs are difficult to reproduce in a journal with all the exquisite refinement of detail of which the electron microscope is capable. If they are engaged in this kind of work, they will have chosen a journal with proved capabilities in fine engraving and printing. Photographs taken through a light microscope are less critical, but should also be examined for high quality, because, in the course of the whole printing process, the image is transferred several times from one surface to another and loses a little sharpness at each transfer.

Once the photographs have been chosen for quality and for the message they are intended to convey, the author must look at each one separately, from the reader's point of view. He should give the reader as much help as possible, for example by selecting the center of the field to coincide with the center of interest, by cropping the print to a shape suitable for the journal without reduction in size, and by affixing arrows and letters to identify portions of the field and to direct attention to the features of interest. Inclusion of a bar to represent 10 μ, 10 A, or any length appropriate to the scale, in a corner of the photograph rapidly orients the reader even though, when the magnification is given in the legend, it is not strictly necessary.

In addition to the general precepts about legends that you have already given, add here the items that an author must remember to include in legends to micrographs: the type of stain, or other essential treatment used to obtain the image; the identification of every letter attached to the photograph; and the degree of magnification.

CONCLUSION

This chapter has dealt with principles and not with graphic techniques, since in research work—whether it is carried out in university, government department, or industry—the scientist usually has access to technical illustrators with greater experience than he can ever hope to acquire, and he should learn to avail himself of this expert knowledge. But only he, as author, can accurately visualize his readers and foresee the scope and limits of his article. Only he, therefore, can gauge whether to use tables or figures and, if so, which and how many of them; only he can make the multitudinous decisions that lead to well-designed illustrative material. For these decisions he needs training in understanding the *purposes* and *principles* of illustrations. Don't bore your students teaching them how to draw and letter; teach them, rather, how to think.

11
Preparation for
Writing the Doctoral Thesis

YOU SHOULD READ:

Pages 1–31 in:
Almack, John C. 1930. *Research and Thesis Writing*. Houghton Mifflin, Boston.

Pages 1–64 in:
Freedman, Paul. 1960. *The Principles of Scientific Research*. Pergamon Press, Oxford and New York. 2nd ed.

Pages 1–17 in:
McCartney, Eugene S. 1953. *Recurrent Maladies in Scholarly Writing*. University of Michigan Press, Ann Arbor.

Pages 1–18 in:
Peterson, Martin S. 1961. *Scientific Thinking and Scientific Writing*. Reinhold, New York.

When he is preparing to write his doctoral thesis, a graduate student looks, of course, to his own research supervisor for guidance. You, the instructor in scientific writing, may wonder what business you have interfering with this arrangement. It is true that the ultimate responsibility for preparing the student to write his thesis rests with each supervisor. However, you can provide your colleagues with an invaluable starting point in discharging this responsibility if you add to your instruction on writing a journal article some class discussions on writing a thesis. "Is there, in fact, any essential difference between the two writing tasks?" should, I think, be the central question to which these discussions are addressed.

In my opinion, the principles to be applied to writing a thesis are identical with those to be applied to writing a journal article. Both forms call for the same self-discipline, the same hard thinking, and clear, logical, concise writing. Yet, because theses are not subject to the limitations of space imposed by editors of professional journals, the notion has unfortunately got about that the style of writing in scientific theses should be quite different from that in journal articles. The freedom from spatial restriction is too often taken as permission to include every unimportant detail and to prose along in intolerably verbose passages; and the nervous candidate, looking over the efforts of his predecessors, feels obliged to be just as tedious as they were for fear his slim volume will seem trivial by comparison.

Theses do not have to be thick to be scholarly. Most true scholars, remembering the long hours of work needed to attain precision and conciseness, would tend, on the contrary, to give the palm for diligence to writers who are brief—if any such could be found. A single major journal article, in which a great deal of work is represented in condensed form, would in many cases be a better measure of a candidate's performance than the usual kind of dissertation now being accepted. However, it is unlikely that more than a few graduate schools will unshackle themselves from tradition to the extent of accepting published articles in lieu of a dissertation (although this is the practice in Sweden, where the doctorate is by no means less demanding than here). Let us therefore consider how we can retain the dissertation's traditional form but regard it, more rationally, as a piece of scientific writing in which the author must meet the same high standards as in later professional publications.

A convenient classroom approach to this subject is for you to solicit and list on the blackboard characteristics of a journal article and of a doctoral dissertation, as though you intend to define some essential differences between the two forms of writing. A few of the distinguishing characteristics generally ascribed to a thesis are listed in Table 1. After several entries have been tabulated ask the question "Which of these supposed differences are both necessary and useful if the purposes of a thesis are to be fulfilled?" A group discussion of such a list will usually confirm that a thesis differs from a journal article in only a few ways, namely those designated A to C in Table 1. Some notes on these features follow.

A *The thesis is an educational tool.* Educators (and students) often make the mistake of regarding the thesis as a measure of the student's *activity* during the educational period instead of as a measure of his *preparedness* for the professional life that follows. The student therefore tends to describe a multitude of details (like a doctoral student) instead of trying

TABLE 1   *Characteristics of a Thesis*
(*as distinguished from a journal article*)

A thesis:

- A   is an educational tool
- B   is the result of individual, not team, research
- C   may present more than one topic
- D   presents a formal statement of hypothesis
- E   contains a detailed review of the literature
- F   presents all the data obtained in the study
- G   offers an extended and argumentative discussion
- H   summarizes the results and conclusions
- J   lists a comprehensive bibliography

to make his thesis a coherent, concise unit of scientific communication (like a mature scientist). To me this seems contrary to the educational purpose.

B *The thesis is the result of individual research.* This distinguishing feature means that the thesis will bear only one author's name. Since a dissertation represents the student's first individual investigation, it should demonstrate his ability to define a problem, to choose appropriate methods for solving the problem, and to present his results and conclusions clearly and fairly. Convincing demonstration of such ability will result only if the student exercises a strong sense of relevance and functional economy, as we have advocated in the writing of a journal article.

C *The thesis may cover several different approaches to a problem.* Each of these may best be presented as a separate chapter, and in this regard the thesis may resemble a book rather than a journal article. Greater control over consistency is therefore needed, as well as an even more detailed outline to help the student maintain an over-all grasp of the dissertation as it takes shape.

Careful examination of the remaining "distinguishing features" shows that the distinctions they purport to convey are false ones. If (D) a journal article does *not* present a formal hypothesis, it is deficient: many articles fail to communicate, precisely because the hypothesis on which the work is based is not enunciated. Although (E) the dissertation traditionally contains an exhaustive review of the literature, you should make it clear that it is not the place for extensive, uncritical listing of others' results. In a similar manner, the dissertation has traditionally become (F) a repository of all data, often only marginally relevant, that the student has collected. Sometimes, these data might be regarded as potentially useful in the future, and if the student is convinced of this he can allow himself to put them in an appendix—but not in the body of the thesis, which should present results as succinctly as in a journal. An extensive and argumentative discussion (G) may occasionally be allowable in a dissertation, but only within reasonable limits (see below), which are scarcely broader than for an article. The results and conclusions *must* be summarized (H), but this is true of journal articles too; and a comprehensive bibliography (J) is usually much inferior to a selective one if the student wants to demonstrate his scientific discrimination and ability.

Try to guide discussion of these matters in such a way that the students themselves conclude that a concise, closely-reasoned dissertation is better than a bulky one. They will be interested in a description, along the following lines, of the history of the thesis as an educational tool. After that, Webster's excellent definition of a scholar will lead you very neatly into a discussion of the most desirable characteristics of the various sections that scholarly dissertations commonly contain.

What Is a Thesis?

Historically, the thesis has changed considerably—from an oral defense of a proposition by the student against all comers in the university to a written description of research that leads to a hypothesis put forward by the student (1). Skill in the logical written presentation of ideas has replaced skill in disputation as the criterion for judging a student's accomplishment. A demonstrated ability to do independent research has been added to the old requirement that the student master the basic principles of knowledge in a particular field of endeavor. The doctoral thesis, therefore, represents the culmination of several years of intensive effort of education and research, and is an exhibit of the mental prowess of the student.

At this point, you can discuss the several manuals that are available on thesis writing (refs. 2–4), but you should point out that they are primarily concerned with details of format and mechanics of construction. Our concern is more with the mental preparation of the student before the task of writing begins than with the details of writing. Most of the principles of writing dealt with in Chapters 1–8 and 10 of this manual are applicable to the thesis, and will not be repeated here.

You should also introduce the student to the literature available on the philosophy of science (5, 6) and the art of scientific investigation (7). This is a large subject, but it would be useful to the student to review and discuss some of the values of logic, intuition, explanation, and proof in conducting research, and to think about the applications of these concepts of philosophy to a thesis. Such a discussion admittedly expands the scope of the subject to include methods of research, but this is a concrete way of emphasizing that the student must produce a "scholarly dissertation."

What Is Meant by a Scholarly Dissertation?

Webster's Third New International Dictionary gives two contrasting definitions of a scholar. The first is "one who attends a school or studies under a teacher." The second is "one who by long systematic study (as in a university) has gained a high degree of mastery in one or more of the academic disciplines; esp. one who has engaged in advanced study and acquired the minutiae of knowledge in some special field along with accuracy and skill in investigation and powers of critical analysis in interpretation of such knowledge." The second definition is more to our purpose in describing the level of intellectual achievement necessary for the Doctor of Philosophy.

Certain words and phrases stand out as important attributes in Webster's definition, e.g., "high degree of mastery," "accuracy and skill in investigation," and "critical analysis in interpretation," and these can be singled out as the keys to a successful thesis. You should take the time to emphasize that these are characteristics *of the student* and are painstakingly acquired long before the thesis is attempted. These attributes will be seen between the lines of the thesis despite attempts to hide shortcomings by flowery prose, long quotations, and an extensive bibliography. Unless the thesis clearly demonstrates that the student has mastered the subject, is a skilled investigator, and has a critical mind, the thesis can scarcely be judged "a scholarly dissertation."

At this point, you should briefly describe an accepted general format for a doctoral thesis—for example, introduction, methods, results, and discussion. Such a description will be useful in presenting the following ideas concerning scholarship and will offer the student a framework of reference for questions or comments.

How Does One Indicate a "High Degree of Mastery" of a Subject?

The *Introduction* of a thesis is the first item to be read, and its content and presentation will largely determine, in the reader's mind, whether the entire thesis is worth perusing. Many instructions for preparing theses favor separating both a statement of the problem and a review of the literature from the general introduction. This makes neat small paragraphs with tidy subheadings, but is a less effective way of indicating competence in a subject area than a complete integration of these items in one concise answer to two questions: "What is the problem under investigation?" and "Why did you select this one for study?" Here the student has a chance to pick and choose from the assembled mass of good and bad published reports and to construct a rational statement of the problem.

You have an opportunity here to introduce the role of intuition and speculation in developing a working hypothesis. To be acceptable, however, such a hypothesis must be testable, and the student is obliged to present a reasonable plan for such a test. Speculation without testing is to be discouraged; this cardinal principle of science was laid down by William Occam—"theoretical existences are not to be increased without necessity."

Nowadays a complete review of the literature is a physical impossibility for most theses. Any attempt to do this by presenting conflicting sides of all pertinent questions in great detail is not only unsatisfactory; it is strong evidence that the student has learned to read and write, but cannot think. If the student shirks his responsibility for making judgments of the value of published reports in relation to his study, how can he hope to convince the reading committee that he has mastered his subject? At the end of a thorough search of the literature, the student should be better qualified to make these decisions than anyone else. A historical record of all false leads and all mistakes in investigation may make interesting reading to some, but in a thesis such a record sows seeds of doubt as to the competence and self-reliance of the student.

I see no real need for a separate answer to the question "Why did you select this problem for study?" A clear, concise statement of the problem will usually indicate that the study under investigation is part of a more general one that bears a direct relation to a basic principle of science or a pressing human need. If the reader at this point still is asking "Why?" the chances are that the introduction needs some rethinking and then rewriting.

How Does One Indicate "Accuracy and Skill in Investigation"?

All theses should have a section dealing with *Methods and Materials* and the accuracy inherent in the methods. In this section all the excuses are made for errors of omission, faulty techniques, and lack of sufficient data for making meaningful comparisons. It is presumed that a good thesis will have a minimum of these excuses, but some show of humility and an awareness of the fallibility of human endeavor will not be construed by an intelligent reader as a significant weakness.

The student may be excused for a rather lengthy description of methodology, unless the methods are standard and readily available to the reader. If a lengthy description is planned, however, the student must train himself to be considerate of the reader and provide an over-all sketch of how the study was done, so the reader may be sustained through the arid passages or enabled to skip them without serious loss.

The student should be cautioned against being overly critical of the methods finally selected for use. Full analysis and criticism of the methods should be made before the study is attempted. If no rational or possible approach to a study presents itself, the wisest course is to look for another problem. No worse criticism of the skill of an investigator can be heard than "He is a hard worker, but the problem he chose was impossible." Once a problem has been selected, and a reasonable approach has been decided upon, the student should look on the bright side and indicate what can be accomplished with the methods.

The meat of the thesis is found in a section usually indicated as *Results*. Impress upon the student that only the results of *his* investigation are to be put here. Presentation of a mixture of the student's data and other published work leads to utter confusion. It also betrays a lack of confidence: the student seems unsure that he can draw reliable conclusions from his results. A skilled investigator knows beforehand what others have found, has analyzed the omissions and faulty techniques, and has designed his procedures to correct these faults. When the main points of the results are logically presented in the text and corroborated by factual data in tables and figures, there should be no need to beg for confirmation by citing another investigator who found the same or a similar thing to be true.

How Does One Indicate "Critical Analysis in Interpretation"?

When a student comes to the point of discussing his study in relation to previous and future work, he stands naked before his professional mentors. Here is the place where his philosophy, his relationship to his colleagues, his scientific attitude, yes, even his religion, come to the forefront. Here is where the great gamble is taken, if he so desires. A discussion can be very brief and conservative, limited to a few unequivocal statements, and ending with a statement that more needs to be done. Or it can be an ingenious and imaginative discourse on what the study may mean in relation to a major problem in the field. The student here can be granted considerable license in speculative thought, provided he pays due regard to rules of logic and inference, and takes care to remain relevant to his topic. He will not be judged harshly if he chooses the popular, conservative course of action. But neither is he likely to be considered a "thoughtful observer of the contemporary scene" unless he attempts to put his work into the perspective of the present state of knowledge.

What Is a Thesis?

To sum up, a thesis may be likened to the reflection of a portion of the student's mind. It should be a rational discourse on a problem in science. Success in presenting a thesis of words, phrases, and paragraphs will depend to a great extent on the preparation of the mind that conceives it. Training in scientific procedures and philosophy, in reading and writing, and above all in disciplined thinking, thus become an integral part of the image conveyed to the reader.

If I were asked for a single measure of scholarship, a single indicator of disciplined thinking, and therefore the best single criterion of a good thesis, I would put forward a plea for simplicity. This quality is, unfortunately, the one most conspicuously lacking in present-day theses and the one least prized among ambitious young scientists.

"Simplicity, paradoxically, is the outward sign and symbol of depth of thought. It seems to me simplicity is about the most difficult thing to achieve in scholarship and writing. How difficult is clarity of thought, and yet it is only as thought becomes clear that simplicity is possible. When we see a writer belaboring an idea we may be sure that the idea is belaboring him."(8)

REFERENCES

1. Almack, John C. 1930. *Research and Thesis Writing*. Houghton Mifflin, Boston.
2. McCartney, E. S. 1953. *Recurrent Maladies in Scholarly Writing*. University of Michigan Press, Ann Arbor.
3. Campbell, W. G. 1954. *Form and Style in Thesis Writing*. Houghton Mifflin Boston. (Rev. ed. of W. G. Campbell. 1939. *A Form Book for Thesis Writing*.)
4. Turabian, K. L. 1955. *A Manual for Writers of Term Papers, Theses and Dissertations*. University of Chicago Press, Chicago (Rev. ed.).
5. Peirce, Charles S. 1957. *Essays in the Philosophy of Science* (first published 1877–1902), edited by Vincent Tomas. Bobbs-Merrill Co., Inc., Indianapolis.
6. Shapere, Dudley. 1965. *Philosophical Problems of Natural Science*. The Macmillan Co., New York and London.
7. Beveridge, W. I. B. 1957. *The Art of Scientific Investigation*. Heinemann, London, and Norton, New York. 3rd ed.
8. Lin Yutang. 1937. *The Importance of Living*. John Day, Reynal and Hitchcock, New York; Heinemann, London (1938). p. 81.

12

Writing a Research Project Proposal

YOU SHOULD READ:

Merritt, D. H. 1963. "Grantsmanship: An Exercise in Lucid Presentation." *Clin. Res.* 11:375–377.

YOU WILL NEED:

The instructions and application forms for grants from any large government agency.

Like other kinds of scientific writing, the writing of a project proposal demands considerable judgment. If the judgment is to be good, the writer must learn all he can about those who will read the proposal, and keep those readers constantly in mind as he writes. You may feel that your students are at too early a stage in their careers to be interested in learning how to write project proposals, and it is true that their first journal article will probably be more imminent than their first grant application. But they will enjoy the logic of applying to this easily imagined task the principles of scientific writing given in Chapters 2–8, and if you show them, by using the project proposal as an example, that the steps you have taught them for writing a journal article can be applied to other kinds of writing, you will have done them a great service.

Project proposals differ according to the audience addressed. For example, a description of some proposed research may be submitted to one's immediate superiors directing the research, who may be expected to be familiar with all the details, or to a group of nonscientific directors conscious of, and knowledgeable about, only far-reaching objectives. Or the project proposal may be a grant application submitted more impersonally to a private foundation or to a government agency. Whoever the recipients of a project proposal may be, they will certainly be more concerned with wider aspects of policy than is the writer of the proposal.

For this reason, the writer must be even more concerned with *summarizing* features than when he is writing a journal article. Thus, he should give still more attention to his title and his abstract, which should be not only concisely descriptive and clearly purposeful, but provocative and stimulating as well. After all, he hopes to interest his readers in the proposal, and convince them it is worthwhile. He should plan to include a Contents page, both for easy reference and to give the reader a bird's-eye view of the proposal right at the start. A clear Statement of Purpose should be an early feature and a statement of Expected Results a late one—both listed in the Contents page. And it is not too much to add an Outline of long or complex passages at the point where they begin. By the same token, the main contours of the budget can usefully appear long before the detailed breakdown of projected costs.

Having enunciated these general principles, go through Steps 1–25 of Writing a Journal Article and show how, with very little change to suit the circumstances, these steps can be used for guidance in writing a project proposal.

STEP 1:   *What Is the Right Time to Prepare a Proposal?*

Unlike the answer to "What is the Right Time to Publish?" which is often "Later than your inclinations suggest," the answer to this question is "Sooner than you think." Grant applications usually take *at least* six months to be acted on, and a well-prepared application can take two months to put together. Eight months, therefore, seems a minimum to allow before the date on which the work is to begin.

STEP 2:   *What Question Will Be Asked, and What Answers Are Expected?*

Teach your students to put the answers to these queries in writing, in preparation for the all-important Statement of Purpose and of Expected Results.

STEP 3: *What Is the Most Suitable Agency?*

Although in writing a project proposal the author is concerned not with publication but with highly restricted circulation of his document, the question of audience is still of paramount importance. Of course, within a single research organization one has no choice of supporting body, but with outside agencies the case is different. Disabuse your students' minds of the notion that foundations and government agencies are mere offices for the automatic distribution of unlimited funds to those who apply for them; on the contrary, all are guided by policies and purposes that the applicant should study closely before he decides where his best chances of success lie.

It may not be so easy to obtain a succinct statement of purpose and scope from a granting agency as it is from a journal, but you can give some tips to your students on how to deduce what they are. They might consult the latest annual report or other statement of the agency's activities, the list of research projects currently supported, or any of the agency's other publications. Get the students to find out, using a selected list of foundations, what can be discovered by direct inquiry about the scope of a foundation's activity.

STEP 4: *How Is the Project Related to the Existing Body of Knowledge?*

It is essential that the applicant make a good showing when he describes the published investigations framing the one he now proposes. His search of the literature must be thorough and thoughtful, or woe betide him when the application is reviewed. He must demonstrate both irrefutable logic and imaginative insight if he is to persuade hardheaded scientists that a gap remains to be filled or that extensions of established lines of research promise rich scientific rewards. Make clear to your students that the case for the project will have to be tightly argued in the proposal itself; in Step 4 the author prepares himself for this close reasoning by writing down succinctly the basic premises from which he will work and seeing whether they lead convincingly to the plan that he will formulate.

S T E P 5 : *Write the Title and Synopsis*

This first statement of what the proposal will cover and, by implication, what it will leave out, serves the same purpose of drawing up the ground plan as in the journal article. Title and synopsis derive directly from Step 2. The synopsis will be reworked later into the General Project Description that all application forms overtly or implicitly require.

S T E P 6 : *Match Title and Synopsis to the Purpose and Scope of the Chosen Agency*

Your students will by now recognize the value of comparing the definite written form of their proposal (Step 5) with the avowed or patent objectives of the group they hope will support it. From here on the aims and desires of that group should be constantly present in the applicant's mind.

S T E P 7 : *Read the Instructions to Applicants*

Some agencies supply printed application forms with detailed and complete instructions on how they are to be filled out. You should get some of these for your students to study. Other agencies have no forms and frequently base their judgment of the merit of an application, and certainly of the ability of the applicant to carry it out, on the way in which the application is organized. If instructions do exist, they should be carefully studied at this stage, since adherence to them may make all the difference between failure and success.

S T E P 8 : *Decide on the Basic Form of the Proposal*

Again, if application forms are provided, the basic form of the proposal is automatically determined, and the applicant is left to exercise his judgment only in the matter of degree of detail in the various sections. Otherwise, a good basic scheme is: brief introduction, concluding with the statement of purpose; general description of proposal; methods; expected results; and discussion, primarily of the significance of the proposed work with respect to the objectives of the agency applied to. The basic scheme is not grossly different from that of a journal article up to this point. To it must be added evidence of the applicant's ability to carry out the work (his position, previous publications, honors and awards) and the facilities available to him; and, of course, estimates of what the project will cost, with justification where necessary.

STEP 9: *Stock the Section Reservoirs*

Here you can advocate exactly the same method as for writing a journal article.

STEP 10: *Construct Tables and Figures*

In general, tables and figures will be used much less frequently than in a journal article, although the possibility of varying the exposition by tabular or even graphical means should not be ignored.

STEPS 11 and 12: *Construct the Topic and Sentence Outlines*

Because continuity of thought and a logical sequence of ideas are likely to move the readers to favorable action, sound outlines may be even more important in a project proposal than in a journal article. For the same reason urge your students to follow *Step 13*: "Write the first draft of the proposal continuously from beginning to end."

STEP 14: *Introduction and General Description of Project*

For the same reasons given in Chapter 4, the description of work preceding the proposed research should be selective rather than exhaustive, and confined to significant references. The introduction must lead clearly to the project description.

STEP 15: *Construct the List of References As You Go Along*

In most applications it is usual to give references within the text rather than in a separate bibliography, so that the need to check bibliographic details becomes evident of itself. Once again, urge your students to acquire the habit of checking references early.

STEPS 16-18: *Methods, Expected Results, and Discussion Sections*

Most of the principles needed in these sections have already been touched on. Remind your students to think clearly about the purpose of the document: for example, in the Methods section the object is not, as in a journal article, to enable a trained investigator who reads the proposal to do the work, but to demonstrate that the applicant is familiar with the methods available and chooses from them wisely. In Expected Results, exaggerated prognostications should be avoided, but, on the other hand, the wide potential significance of the work must be brought out in the Discussion.

STEPS 19-25

The remaining steps in writing a journal article (see Chapters 5–8) apply almost without change to writing a project proposal. Remind your students what the steps are, and point out that the technique they have learned for one type of scientific writing will stand them in good stead in many others. Impress on them that in the less "scientific" parts of the proposal, those that deal not with the project but with the applicant, they should not allow a feeling of false modesty to lead them into affected circumlocutions, but should maintain the same clean scientific style—brief, simple, and direct— throughout the proposal. Deviousness of any kind is to be avoided, and the applicant's best chance of success, here as in all kinds of scientific writing, lies in honesty and clarity of purpose.

*   *   *

Writing a project proposal is a considerable undertaking. You may decide to give it instead of a journal article as the major assignment of the writing course, as suggested in Chapter 2, or you may make it an additional assignment if time permits. In either case, I suggest that the proposal be written as though for a large governmental agency, such as the National Science Foundation, that does *not* have a prescribed outline, so that the students have maximum freedom in organizing this piece of writing.

Help your students to visualize the audience they are writing for by listing the criteria by which the worth of every application for financial support is judged:

1. Validity of the central concept
2. Soundness of the experimental design
3. Significance on a pure scientific, regional, or national level
4. Relevance to the over-all program of the funding agency
5. Competence of the personnel who are to carry out the project
6. Adequacy of the research facilities
7. Appropriateness of the budget (remember to point out that too modest a budget can be as damaging as an overblown one in indicating the applicant's poor judgment)
8. Inclusion of an evaluation mechanism, if appropriate. How will the degree of success of the project be assessed? The more original or daring the project, the more it ventures into virgin territory, the more need there is to devise a workable and effective program of evaluation.

13

Oral Presentation of a
Scientific Paper

EDITOR'S PREFACE:

Some justification may seem necessary for including a chapter about speaking in a book about writing. We do not intend, however, to be apologetic about this inclusion because no one will dispute that formal talks at local, national, or international meetings are often closely linked—as elements in the transmission of knowledge—with publication of the same work in an archival journal. From an organizational point of view, planning an article and planning a talk are identical up to a certain point, while the same principles of scientific style apply throughout. Didactically, the juxtaposition of a course on writing with a subsequent short course on oral presentation is excellent for teaching the similarities and differences between the two modes of communication. Finally, the writing that is necessary in the early stages of planning a talk provides yet another concrete example for your students of the postulate (see Chapter 2) that writing clarifies thought.

TIMING:

Three to four one-hour sessions are sufficient. Principles can be dealt with, and exemplified by a 10-minute talk of your own, in the first two hours; in each subsequent hour three ten-minute talks can be given by the students and critically discussed, as explained in the chapter. These "rehearsal" sessions can be continued as long as you think them useful to the nonperformers (they are always useful to the performers).

YOU WILL PROBABLY FIND THE FOLLOWING
MATERIAL USEFUL:

American Chemical Society. 1961. *Suggestions on How to Organize, Present and Illustrate a Technical Paper*. Bulletin 8, available ($1.00, or 50c each on orders of 10 or more copies) from the Society at 1155 16th Street, N.W., Washington, D.C. 20036.

Casey, Robert S. 1958. *Oral Communication of Technical Information*. Reinhold, New York and London.

Hays, Robert. 1965. "Including visual aids in reports." Chapter 10 of *Principles of Technical Writing*. Addison-Wesley, Reading, Mass.

Jones, B. A. 1954. "The oral report, its preparation and presentation." Chapter 7 of *The Technical Report* (Benjamin H. Weil, editor). Reinhold, New York and London.

Norgaard, M. 1959. "The text of a speech." Chapter 11, Section XV of *Technical Writer's Handbook*. Harper and Bros., New York.

Weiss, H., and J. B. McGrath, Jr. 1963. *Technically Speaking*. McGraw-Hill, New York and London.

Oral communication plays an important part in the exchange of scientific information. The main purpose of a congress—oral discussion between participants—can be achieved only if a contribution is heard and understood. Scientists often travel thousands of miles to a congress, and each participant should feel duty-bound to be informative, interesting, and concise.

A delivered paper can have a dismal reception for many reasons, but often the main one is that because the proceedings of the conference are to be published, the speaker mistakenly regards his talk as a form of publication. He prepares the talk carefully, and dutifully reads it word for word from his manuscript. Students may be very ready to accept your statement that this is not recommended, but it is well worth the time to discuss with them why it is a bad practice. Point out the differences between oral and written communication—the finite attention span of a listener, the frequent presence of distractions in the auditorium, the inability of a listener to go back over a difficult sentence or to request that an inaudible one be repeated—and show how these considerations should induce the potential speaker to:

1. Capture the full attention of the audience at the very beginning.
2. State the underlying objectives of the research with even greater clarity and emphasis than in written articles.
3. Concentrate on concepts, and eliminate confusing details.
4. Discuss the purpose of each experiment, the conclusions drawn from it, and its connection with the main argument at the time that the results are shown, rather than in a separate "Discussion" section.

5. Present important ideas in several different ways, even at the risk of repetition (an undesirable trait in written presentation).
6. Use slides of lesser complexity than published figures and tables.

This chapter suggests some of the ground rules for an effective oral presentation. Most of what follows is applicable to a 10- or 15-minute presentation, since such short periods are frequently allotted for papers at large-scale scientific meetings. If a student can master the 10-minute talk, he should have little trouble—except, perhaps, that of providing variety of pace and pitch—with longer talks, for the difficulty most people experience consists not in finding enough to say but in condensing what they have to say into the time allowed.

Organization

Should one write out the talk? Yes, but never read it (the reasons will be discussed later). Once the talk is organized through writing, the text can be reduced to an outline. But it should be written out first, rather than simply outlined, so that one can (a) check the logical development, (b) ensure proper transitions, (c) check sentence length and thereby develop the habit of forming short conversational sentences, (d) search for synonyms for frequently recurring words that would otherwise lead to dullness, (e) discard attractive but inessential items, (f) develop colorful imagery, and (g) ensure that only familiar terms are used.

The shorter the time for an oral presentation, the more difficult is the task of organization. From the beginning, train your students to proportion their time correctly: 10 percent for the introduction, 80 percent for the body of the talk (procedure, results, and conclusions), and 10 percent for the summary.

THE INTRODUCTION

A speaker often has many things to contend with at the outset. Rooms get overheated and smoky, and the audience may be restive after listening to previous speakers. People may be moving about in the rear of the room, greeting incoming or outgoing friends, rustling the pages of their programs, coughing, and so forth. The opening words of a speech must, therefore, be simple, easily understood, and carefully slanted toward the interests of the audience. One secret of speaking successfully to a large audience is to gain attention with the opening sentences; otherwise it may never be secured at all.

The part of the introduction that precedes the statement of purpose is called the *approach to the audience* because its aim is to arouse interest, to create a friendly and receptive mood, and to prepare the audience to listen and pay attention to the statement of purpose.

Many devices can be employed to capture audience attention, and students should be encouraged to invent examples. Opening with a *narrative* arouses interest because people like to hear stories. ("There is a story of two protein chemists who, encountering each other at the Biochemical Congress in Tokyo, got into an argument about . . . ," or, "One of the most appealing stories in the history of organic chemistry is the one in which Kekulé, jolting along on top of a London bus, suddenly envisioned the benzene molecule in the form of a snake with its tail in its mouth. Unfortunately, the story is inaccurate.")

Opening with a *quotation* is effective if one is chosen that is relevant to the speech and points toward a direct statement of the speaker's purpose. ("Shortly after argon had been discovered, Lord Rayleigh said 'I have seen some indications that the anomalous properties of argon are brought as a kind of accusation against us. But we had the very best intentions in the matter. The facts were too much for us, and all that we can do now is to apologize for ourselves and for the gas. . . .' A somewhat similar situation has arisen with respect to the X-protein, the anomalous properties of which have formed the basis of several unjust accusations. Would it not be preferable to recognize the anomalies, and try to explain them?")

A *rhetorical question* centers attention on the purpose of the study and makes the audience think about the main issue. ("How much do we really know of the mechanism whereby DNA directs the synthesis of RNA?")

Sometimes a *startling statement* will jolt the audience into paying attention. ("Reading our most distinguished scientific journals corrupts the minds of young scientists," or, "Cell membranes seem to be wide open to penetration by all sorts of noxious substances—that is, if you consider them merely as physicochemical barriers.")

A *negative statement* will heighten the "suspense." ("Lowering blood cholesterol levels will not prevent atherosclerosis. At least, there has been no good evidence for this so far.")

A *comparison or contrast* makes a neat opening, particularly if the contrast is a striking one. ("In former times, delicate ladies were carried through the doors of opera houses in sedan chairs to avoid being jostled by the crowd. We are concerned here today with the concept of *carrier molecules* that will transport particular substances safely through the hurlyburly of the cell membrane," or, "Few phenomena are so well understood thermodynamically, or so ill understood kinetically, as the osmotic flow of a solvent through a semipermeable membrane.")

If the speaker knows the *dominant interest* of his audience, he can use it to establish an understanding with them. ("We are all familiar with the thesis that bats use some form of radar to navigate in the darkness. I would like today to offer a novel and unrelated explanation of their skill in avoiding objects under these conditions.")

The attention of a group can usually be caught by listing *specific instances* that relate to a general topic. ("Molecules can pass through a membrane by passive diffusion, or by dissolving in the membrane lipids, or by active transport. Which of these applies to the absorption of bile salts in man?")

Other introductory devices include the practice of starting with a broad statement and *gradually narrowing* it to lead into the purpose of the study being reported; the *descriptive opening* (best suited to papers dealing with new equipment, new techniques, etc.); and the *historical approach.*

Speakers on nontechnical subjects customarily open their talks with a funny story. The pseudohumor of the stock joke ("a funny thing happened to me on the way to the convention hall") is likely to fall flat on its face before an audience of scientists. However, the more subtle humor of asides interpolated throughout the speech is to be encouraged. Still other introductory possibilities include the asking of a question, which the speaker then proceeds to answer immediately; the listing of a series of particulars or a set of vivid details to provide transition to the main thesis; and the use of analogy, where the unknown is paralleled with the known. Examples of several types of openings for a single talk are given in the appendix (pages 165 and 166) to this chapter.

The most obvious device, of course, is to open with a statement of the speaker's purpose. This is certainly one of the most useful when the audience is known to have a direct interest in the topic. However, there are dangers in this straightforward and commonsense approach, which rests on three assumptions: that the listeners have a consuming interest in the topic;

that they have actually heard and understood the title of the talk and studied a previously published abstract; and that they have a thorough knowledge of work on the topic to date. These assumptions may be far from true.

Having (it is to be hoped) captured the interest of the audience, the speaker must state clearly the underlying objectives of the work—why it is of interest—and then give the exact purpose of the experiments to be described. The purpose may be quite a small part of the over-all objectives. There is no shame in this; indeed, the shorter the talk, the more circumscribed the purpose should be. Nothing is more foolish and arrogant than the sickly "Of course I can't really compress four years of work into 15 minutes, but I'll try." The speaker has not been asked to do so, and he has no right to insult his audience by attempting it.

BODY OF THE TALK

Make it clear to your students that the body of a talk requires much the same logical organization of material as an article prepared for publication. The principles of style given in Chapter 6 apply with equal or greater force here. Ideas must be conveyed in short, clear statements (Rule 1). Words must be chosen and used appropriately and precisely (Rule 2) if the listeners are not to be distracted or misled. Vivid language can transform a prosaic talk into a memorable one and speakers should strive to avoid abstract nouns (Rule 3) and to use active rather than passive verbs. The terms used must be readily comprehensible (Rule 4). If the speaker feels that definition of a term is necessary, he must give the definition when the term is first mentioned, taking care not to sound patronizing as he does so.

The purpose of each experiment should be stated and related to the over-all purpose given in the Introduction. This takes time, but the time is well spent because the audience is really in touch with the thread of the argument. Because the time for presentation is limited and the audience is mostly interested in concepts, experimental details must be kept to an absolute minimum. They can always be elicited later during the question-and-answer period when the audience takes the initiative, and, of course, they can be provided in a printed text.

In stating the conclusions from each experiment, the speaker should keep the main purpose of the study in mind and ensure that every point he makes is related to that purpose.

VISUAL AIDS

Visual aids can be effective in maintaining interest, but only if they are used with judgment. They range from a simple tool like the blackboard to complex methods of slide or movie projection. Your students will welcome some discussion of their usefulness and disadvantages.

The use of the blackboard should be confined to small rooms, for people in the back must be able to decipher the message. Blackboard explanations should be planned in advance so that the first part of algebraic symbols or equations or lists will *not* have to be erased to make room for the last parts. Bits of information should not be jotted down in corners of the board, with sweeping lines to indicate where they should have been written in the first place. If circumstances permit, blackboard demonstrations should be *executed* in advance as well, otherwise much valuable time may be lost while the speaker is writing.

Illustrative slides are the most popular form of visual aids, but they, too, pose problems (see Table 1). Remember that slides take time; the audience must be able to understand them fully. At the very least, 1 minute must be allowed for showing and describing a slide, unless it is an extremely simple one shown for a single effect. Demonstrate by example why a graph is preferable to a table and why a simple graph is preferable to one cluttered with more detail than the audience can easily absorb. Let students practice writing captions that are both descriptive and concise and insist that axes be labeled in letters that can be read easily.

Audiences should not be left in the dark throughout the talk, but having the lights constantly flipped on and off can also be distracting. The best compromise is to show well-defined groups of slides, with the lights on between groups. When the speaker wants to provide many data, he will be well advised to show only a small group of slides and supplement them with handouts distributed after the talk (not before, or they, too, will distract the audience's attention!).

The disadvantage of most projection techniques is that while the slide is being projected it replaces the speaker. A notable exception is overhead projection; it complements the speaker because he controls the machine while facing the audience in normal lighting. He can use separate components of a transparency ("vugraphs") to build up a composite image or to disclose information progressively. The versatility of vugraphs in simulating

TABLE 1 *Use of Slides*

Design

Do	Don't
Allow at least 1 min per slide	Make too many points per slide
Allow time for getting slide on and off	Plan too many slides for time allotted
Allow for accidents to happen	Use tables when graphs are more vivid
Provide titles for slides	Put too many lines on a graph
Plan exactly what to say about each slide	Use unlabeled axes

Technique of making the slide

Do	Don't
Select standard size (2 x 2 or 3¼ x 4 inches)	Use illegibly small numbers
Make material fit a rectangle with long side horizontal	Use square or tall slides unless unavoidable
Use colors if helpful, but not for doubtful esthetic effect	Use white letters on blue or black ground*
Label micrographs to direct audience to point of interest	Use poor-quality prints accompanied by an apology
	Use typewritten slides unless lettered ones are absolutely unavailable†

Presentation

Do	Don't
Ensure slides are in correct order and all the same way up	Keep audience continuously in dark
Locate the pointer before talk	Keep flicking lights off and on
Switch off a flashlight arrow pointer after each use	Continue to show slide after it is needed
Show slide long enough for comprehension	Read aloud every word on the slide

* Some practitioners maintain stoutly that these "negative" slides are more legible than those with black letters on a white ground. In order not to be dogmatic about it, have your students use the experimental approach and judge for themselves between examples of the same slide made both ways and shown under good and bad conditions in a completely darkened or partly illuminated hall.

† Typewritten slides *can* be legible if all the material that is to be photographed on a 3¼ x 4 inch slide is kept within a rectangle 56 spaces (4.8 inches) wide by 22 spaces (3.7 inches) high, and if a reversed carbon paper is placed behind the paper during the typing. Hand lettering is almost always preferable, however, because the ratio of black lettering to white "blank space" can be increased and because many different sizes of letters can be used.

motion makes them ideal for describing various biological processes.

The professionals in the field of visual aids are the technical illustrators employed by most large institutions. Even if a scientist has mastered the art of graphic presentation in a written article, there is no guarantee that he is also a master at selecting the lettering that will project best. Encourage your students to consult professional illustrators and heed their advice. Too often these artists complain, and with justification, that "every author is an Art Director—he thinks!"

SUMMARY OF THE TALK

The talk should end with a summary of the ideas presented and leave the audience with the central theme firmly in their minds. Devices for ending the talk include restressing the main points, restating the thesis, concluding with an anecdote, concluding with a question, and concluding by stating a future program.

OUTLINING THE TALK

Once you have impressed upon your students the need for careful preparation and writing of a scientific talk, disabuse their minds of the notion that the talk should be read exactly as written. A speaker cannot hope to hold an audience if he buries his head in a text, raising it only occasionally to reassure himself that he is not alone in the room. Technical material is difficult enough for listeners to absorb without the additional burden of boredom. Train your students, then, to speak either entirely without notes or from a simple outline.

The three most common types are the topic outline, the key-phrase outline, and the sentence outline. The inexperienced speaker is well advised to construct all three in order to fix the organization of the talk in his mind in three different ways. The extent to which a speaker can free himself from the prepared text is usually in direct ratio to his experience as a public speaker. The experienced speaker writes and revises his speech, fixes the main points of the organization in his mind along with some of the key sentences, and uses only a few cards to refresh his memory. On these cards (5 x 7 inches, not smaller) may be written topic headings, key sentences, or transitional sentences; speakers differ on which they find most useful. Suggest to your students that they try all three types. The cards are merely a device to keep the talk in sequence and to avoid the hazards of suddenly going blank. They are the visible end-product of much careful planning, the most important product of which is invisible—a mental image of the intention, structure, and conclusions of the projected talk.

Delivery

Nothing destroys a well-organized talk faster than its delivery in a mumbled monotone by a speaker who obviously wishes he were anywhere except on the platform. Deadly delivery, unintentional punctuation with ah's and er's, and nervous mannerisms evoke an audience reaction ranging from boredom to acute sympathetic embarrassment. All are obstacles that keep the audience from getting the message. Practice and more practice is the solution (more on this in the next section of the chapter).

SPEAKING RATE, FORCE, AND PITCH

Justly or not, an audience is prone to judge a speaker in great part by the way he sounds. Granting that there is a tremendous range in natural ability, each speaker can, with a little training, make better use of his voice mechanism.

Because good speaking implies that the listeners should be able to think along with the speaker as he talks, a proper speaking rate is essential. It takes practice to avoid talking so quickly that the words are slurred. On the other hand, phrases should not be so dragged out that the audience yearns to supply the words.

The force used in delivery is as important as the rate. In a room that has no provision for mechanical amplification, the best rule is to talk to the people in the back row. Both force and pitch should be varied in a way that emphasizes the main ideas and important parts of the talk, and the longer the talk is to be the more planning should go into this variation. A deadly monotone should be avoided at all costs; the room is probably stuffy enough without giving the audience an additional reason for drifting off to sleep.

MICROPHONE TECHNIQUE

The increasing availability of mechanical aids permits a speaker to use a more natural voice and still be heard in the back row. However, the mere presence of a microphone does not guarantee that his words will be understood, and amplification emphasizes the speaker's faults as well as any pleasing qualities his voice may have.

Coach your students to stand at least six inches from the microphone; the optimum distance will depend on the strength and quality of a particular voice and on the type of microphone. Have them speak in a natural voice and move away from the instrument slightly when they reach points they wish to emphasize by raising their voices. This will avoid undue amplification. Stress that they must *never* cough or clear their throats directly into the microphone unless they want to sound like the mating call of a bull elephant.

Practice will prevent "mike fright" and ensure that the instrument is a help rather than a hindrance. Once the microphone technique has been acquired, the instrument can be ignored. Be sure your students don't talk directly to it; once they have lost eye contact, they have lost the audience.

Eye Contact

The inexperienced speaker is greatly tempted to look at the floor, the ceiling, out of the window—anywhere, in fact, except at his audience. But eye contact is absolutely essential to effective speaking. One helpful piece of advice is to tell the speaker to pick out several individuals in the audience and speak directly to them in turn—a man near the back row, a lady who looks as though her feet hurt, a man who seems in danger of falling asleep. If he can hold *their* interest, he has it made!

Posture

Posture is a comparatively minor part of delivery, but good posture can contribute much to the impression of relaxation, and the more relaxed the speaker appears to be, the more the audience will be at ease. Warn your students, however, against being excessively informal (hands in pockets, tucked into the belt, etc.), for this can be offensive to a distinguished audience. There is no standardized recommended posture, but there are certain awkward positions that you can help your students avoid. Standing with heels together and toes pointed out at a 45-degree angle tends to make the speaker's legs look tied together. Standing with feet wide apart, as though weathering a gale, will cause a rocking motion that is highly distracting to the audience. A natural stance results when the feet are placed 8 to 10 inches apart, one foot slightly forward of the other. This permits the weight to rest on the foot in back and allows a natural, easy movement when the speaker wants to walk toward the audience or move to right or left. Walking should always be planned and purposeful; aimless wandering about may relax the speaker, but not his listeners.

GESTURES

An untrained speaker is extremely self-conscious about gestures and regards them as theatrical. Assure him that the complete absence of gesture is still *more* unnatural, because it suggests that he is made of stone, incapable of moving arms or legs and even of changing facial expression. Train him to let his arms hang naturally, not stiffly, and to move fluently from this position into the most frequently used gesture—pointing to a slide. The ability to locate and point to a portion of a slide while continuing to face the audience and to speak smoothly and coherently is fundamental to good oral presentation.

Ask your students to observe their colleagues in an informal conference. A man smoking a pipe or holding a pencil will gesture with it from time to time to emphasize a point; such gestures are spontaneous and come as a result of his concentration on what he is saying. Some gestures gracefully underline the speaker's words; others, even though unrelated to the subject matter, are somehow reassuring. Gestures in an informal talk should give an equally natural impression, although in point of fact they must be on a larger scale in a lecture theatre if they are not to appear puny or perfunctory.

NERVOUS TENSION

It is natural for any speaker to feel some nervous tension when he faces an audience. A certain amount may actually be beneficial by acting as a mental spur. However, nervous gestures and visibly quaking knees disturb the audience. A rostrum is a handy gadget for concealing nervousness and awkward posture, but it should not be clung to as though in desperation. Absolute mastery of one's feelings seldom comes even with much practice in public speaking. However, there are ways to reduce nervousness. The most important one, of course, is to know the subject thoroughly, to be

completely sure of the outline, and to have prepared and rehearsed so
thoroughly that absolutely nothing major can go wrong.

Advise a student not to start speaking as soon as he reaches the platform; instead, tell him to relax by taking several deep breaths. Then have
him concentrate on his outline, pause slightly between paragraphs, and
speak deliberately but in a normal tone of voice. Remind him that the
listeners are sympathetic and want him to do his best. At worst, they are
neutral toward him personally, having come in the hope of gleaning useful
information. A single warm, friendly smile at the beginning does wonders
to relax both the speaker and the audience.

TIMING

As timing is so important, timing marks should be inserted into the organizational plan of the talk; changed, if necessary, during each rehearsal by a
colleague listening with stop-watch in hand; and finally marked in red on
the file cards used for the performance. If nervousness has made the speaker
go faster or slower during the actual talk than during the rehearsal sessions,
the timing marks will bring this to his attention early enough to make the
appropriate correction.

A speaker who is neither hurrying nor dallying requires about one
minute for 120 words. The equivalent of a double-spaced typewritten page
will take roughly 2½ minutes to present. This allows time for brief pauses
after important points.

A technique used by news commentators and other professional
speakers will stand all speakers in good stead: rather than using a simple
period at the end of each sentence, they place a series of periods at the end
of principal thoughts. These are reminders to pause and allow time for
audience comprehension.

GETTING OFF THE PLATFORM

When inexperienced speakers realize they are nearing the end of a talk,
they are likely to speed up the rate of delivery as though they cannot wait to
finish and rush off—which, indeed, may well be the case!

Because the end of a speech should be its strongest point, the conclusion should be rounded out and the final sentence delivered in a firm

voice. Train a student to avoid asking for questions when he finishes. In the first place, this is the chairman's responsibility; second, it precludes applause; and third, it takes the listeners' thoughts away from the speaker's final sentence.

Taking one step back after the final words and looking at the chairman is a good plan. This enables the speaker to pick up his outline during the applause and saves him from the final indignity of having to retrieve cards or papers that can be scattered far and wide by a hasty retreat.

Rehearsal

An instructor can render a lasting service to his students not only by convincing them of the importance of thorough preparation for oral communication, but also by providing opportunities for practice in giving talks. A first step in developing effective speaking techniques is to organize working sessions in which one student gives a 10-minute talk, with the rest of the class *at the back* of a lecture room to serve as audience. Familiarity with the subject is the best way to avoid nervousness, so topics should be carefully selected—one that ties in with part of a student's major assignment from the writing course, or a description of some other research he has conducted, or a "journal club" presentation summarizing one or more papers in which the speaker is particularly interested. You can gain the confidence of your class and create an atmosphere of constructive criticism by leading off with a 10-minute talk yourself and inviting criticism. If you don't want your self-image to be too badly bruised, insert some deliberate errors in both speech and slides to permit the criticism to have a starting point and a focus.

When tape recorders are available, they should be recommended for solo rehearsal sessions. Their usefulness is, however, limited, because the delivery may sound slow to the practicing student when actually it is the proper speed for audience absorption.

Classroom practice sessions serve a function that no amount of solitary practice can. They provide the "live" audience essential for rehearsing eye contact, gestures, and other aspects of platform ease. The question-and-answer period following his presentation can pinpoint the weaknesses in a student's talk, particularly by showing him the points he failed to make clear and those he should have emphasized more.

There will be times when questions directed to the speaker strike him as stupid or even malicious. Tell him to make sure he has heard the question correctly. Asking that it be repeated also gives him additional time to marshal his thoughts and phrase his response. If a courteous and informative reply is not accepted, the speaker can suggest meeting his questioner later so they can go into more detail without bogging down the session or running over the allotted time.

The question period can also prepare him for the shock of an unresponsive audience. It is most disheartening to conclude what one feels was an effective presentation and have total silence in response to the chairman's request for questions. One question is usually all it takes to get an audience started. The student will do well to furnish one or two of his close friends with questions he would like to be asked. Their questions not only get things moving but also give him an opportunity to provide more detail on a point than time limitations allowed in his formal presentation. This device, incidentally, is often employed at large-scale congresses by scientists who have gained recognition as effective speakers.

Criticism of a student's initial efforts should come mainly from the instructor and they should be constructive. Greater frankness can come later! Class seminars make a useful forum in which the fledgling speaker can gain confidence before venturing farther afield, and they prepare him for the unsuspected hazards of oral presentation—the disappearing chalk, the unadjustable microphone, slides that persist in being out of order or upside down, and fainting or other disturbances in the audience.

Something that students find most surprising is that success in presenting serious, scholarly work depends to a considerable extent on techniques borrowed from the theatre. Coach the shyest and most introspective of your students to give his short talk in an overemphatic, theatrical way, with a degree of projection that he considers inappropriate, and ask for the class's reactions. If the lecture room is any bigger than a classroom, the chances are that the class will think it a refreshingly clear performance, not in the least exaggerated. Even the tape recording will reveal to the distrustful performer that he is by no means a candidate for an Oscar, but has merely given—perhaps for the first time in his life—a talk with the firm, strong delivery that it deserves.

APPENDIX TO CHAPTER 13

Examples of possible openings for the topic *The Epidemiology of Frostbite*, suitable for many different types of audience.

THE NARRATIVE

"The typical sergeant in Korea during the winter of 1951–52 was a mother hen. He coaxed, pleaded, cajoled, and ordered his men to change their socks often, to cleanse their feet as often as possible, to keep moving their toes and fingers as much as possible when pinned down by enemy fire. A man so eager to have his men do such things is not likely to forget to do them himself. Small wonder, then, that the rate of frostbite among sergeants *as identical risks* was 4.2 per 1,000 compared to 13.0 for privates."

RHETORICAL QUESTION

"Why did so many American fighting men suffer frostbite in Korea during the winter of 1950? Was it because Uncle Sam was unprepared? Was it that Uncle Sam just didn't care?"

STARTLING STATEMENT

"Alcohol is the most successful protection against frostbite—alcohol taken internally and in large quantities. Or so we might be led to believe from newspaper stories of drunks who peacefully survived a night in an alley under winter temperatures that could be expected to kill an average person."

NEGATIVE STATEMENT

"Improved standards of clothing developed on the basis of World War II did not prevent cold injury during the Korean conflict. Improved equipment designed for better operation in freezing temperatures did not prevent cold injury during the Korean conflict. And training techniques in effect from the lessons of World War II failed to prevent cold injury during the Korean conflict."

COMPARISON OR CONTRAST

"The United States Army often awards the Purple Heart to soldiers who have incurred frostbite. The British Army is more apt to slap their men with a charge of malingering."

REFERENCE TO AUDIENCE'S DOMINANT INTEREST

"All of you here this morning have a special interest in cold injury. Some of you have made important contributions to that general area, either by categorizing degrees of severity of injury or by delineating treatment regimes. But I wonder how many of you have given thought to such subtle modifying factors as fatigue and morale."

LISTING OF SPECIFIC INSTANCES

"A frontline rifleman is more apt to suffer frostbite than a cook at Division headquarters. An inadequately clad soldier is much more susceptible to frostbite than one who is warmly clad. But how do we explain the fact that one soldier suffers frostbite while another, wearing the same type of combat clothing and in the same immediate locale, does not? What, in insurance language, is it that makes one a better risk than another?"

GRADUAL NARROWING OF BROAD STATEMENT

"Weather conditions during the 1950 police action in Korea were probably the most severe ever faced by the American fighting man. Winter temperatures were lower than those in Europe during World War I or in either Europe or the Aleutians during World War II."

DESCRIPTIVE OPENING

"For the first time in field research into cold injury under combat conditions, finite temperatures and wind speeds were measured along the front lines. The separation of data according to intensity of combat permitted formulas to be devised that were reasonably reliable in predicting the incidence of frostbite under other conditions."

HISTORICAL APPROACH

"Historical reference to cold injury in war goes back many centuries. The armies of Alexander the Great experienced it, as did Napoleon's forces in Russia. Indeed, cold continued to be an effective ally of the Russians in World War II, as can be attested by any German soldier who survived a Russian winter."

14

Principles and Practices
in Searching the
Scientific Literature

EDITOR'S PREFACE:

This chapter has been placed at the end of the book because it does not fit readily into a course on scientific writing given to advanced graduate students. Clearly, if your students are ready to contemplate writing a journal article they must have been engaged in research for a year or two; they should already be fairly skilled in searching the literature and will have been guided in bibliographic techniques by their individual supervisors at the outset of their research.

But because searching the literature is so closely related to contributing to it, we have included this outline for teaching the subject formally, and suggest these alternative times for offering it:

A. At the beginning of the graduate student's career, as a way of familiarizing him quickly with search techniques and convenient sources of information. Each supervisor of research could teach his new students individually, using this outline, or the instructor in scientific writing could teach a class in general principles as a basis for individual supervisors' later refinement.

B. As part of the course on scientific writing in the student's second or third year of research. The material would then come as reinforcement or review of whatever guidance was provided at the beginning of the research. Two fresh approaches can now be employed, both because of the student's experience in library work and because of his exposure to the principles and process of scientific writing. In one, the instructor concentrates on the *writing* that the literature searcher does in the library: effective note-taking, combination of the conclusions of several papers into a short survey, and all other kinds of critical analysis on paper—with reference to the principle that *writing clarifies thinking*. The other approach is to get the students to analyze the difficulties they encounter in their search and thereby define how the author of a journal article, by taking appropriate thought as he writes, can facilitate a searcher's access to the information and ideas he will publish. In designing his title, abstract, and key indexing terms, the student will then have a more extensive audience in mind than those who will read his article immediately on publication, and in one more way he will be trained to do a better job of writing a journal article than before he followed this course.

YOU SHOULD READ:

Downs, R. B. 1966. *How to Do Library Research*. University of Illinois Press, Urbana.

Mudge, I. G. Introduction to C. M. Winchell's *Guide to Reference Books* (7th ed.), American Library Association, Chicago, 1951. (The Introduction appeared first in the 6th edition, 1936, compiled by Mudge.)

NOTE: References on the subject of searching the scientific literature offer either general principles or certain specific pieces of information, such as comments on *Index Bergeyana* for bacterial nomenclature. Few, if any, specific guidelines on "how to do it" are to be found for a search of a single narrow field, such as the literature on food additives. To assist moderately specialized students, you might explore:

Biological

Bottle, R. T., and H. V. Wyatt. 1967. *The Use of Biological Literature*. Butterworth, London; Shoe String Press, Hamden, Conn.

Kerker, A. E., and H. T. Murphy. 1968. *Biological and Biomedical Resource Literature*. Purdue University, Lafayette, Ind.

Medical

Fleming, T. P. 1960. *A Guide to the Medical Literature*. Columbia University Press, New York.

Morton, L. T. 1952. *How to Use a Medical Library*. Heinemann Medical, London. (Primarily for British users.)

Sewell, W. 1957. "The Retrieval of Therapeutic Information: Using Abstract and Index Publications." *Special Libraries*. 48:189–193.

Chemical

Burman, C. R. 1965. *How to Find Out in Chemistry*. Pergamon Press, Oxford and New York.

Bottle, R. T. (ed.) 1962. *Use of the Chemical Literature*. Butterworths, London; Shoe String Press, Hamden, Conn.

Mathematical

Pemberton, J. E. 1964. *How to Find Out in Mathematics*. Pergamon Press, Oxford and New York.

Although searching the literature is long established as the scientist's way of ensuring that he knows what others have done in the experimental quest for knowledge, the budding behavioral sciences have not as yet produced a theory of search. Habits and patterns of searching the literature vary with individual inquiries, interests, settings, resources, temperaments, schedules, and budgets in the world of science.

There seems to be, then, no single "right way" to search the literature and keep up to date with it. Nevertheless, there are some valid general principles of search, and by enunciating them you can help each student to choose his own tactics wisely, in the full knowledge of what is available and what is likely to suit him best. Emphasize that he has a multitude of alternatives and should choose among them deliberately. I have arranged this chapter in two sections—*Principles* and *Practices*—in the hope that you, too, will pick and choose, selecting from both sections what seems most appropriate and useful for your class. Similarly, the assignments are suggested at logical places in the text but need not be assigned in this order or, indeed, used at all unless you have the time and the wish to illustrate the particular points to which they refer.

Variations in search patterns depend not only on the factors mentioned above but also on the phase of search. At the earliest phase, search is exploratory. It may begin with the reading of a review to develop direction and perspective. The oriented reader will then zero in on a favored target with the aid of a bibliography chosen as a result of this preliminary reading. When he has selected the area in which research seems called for and likely to be fruitful, he will develop a hypothesis and then look specifically for accounts of previous work that bears on this hypothesis. Finally, he must keep up with new findings. In this phase, he consults colleagues, reads specialized journals, and screens abstracts. The selection of a special subject may sharply reduce the volume of literature he feels he should cover. Even for browsing outside the chosen field, a few outstanding journals usually enable the reader to follow the mainstream of science. Screening techniques and other search devices can help the student mine and refine the literary ore.

While the teacher is wise to emphasize that search of the literature must precede experiment, it may also be useful to caution the student against being discouraged when he finds that his best ideas seem to have been preempted by his elders. If his question is well conceived, it is probable that he will find some aspect of it that may be untouched or that requires re-examination, for the published literature is not without flaws. In that case the search, far from being fruitless, will have provided the necessary background for continuing investigation. In any event, the student should be encouraged to pursue a line of inquiry that promises to open new avenues as he progresses.

If you are giving a self-contained course on searching the literature, you may like to entitle it "Use of the Literature Before, During, and At the End of a Piece of Research," in order to emphasize how search technique changes with the phase of research. If, on the other hand, you are adding the "search" sessions to the writing course described in Part 1 of this manual, the point at which you choose to insert this instruction (see the preface to this chapter) will affect which type of search strategy you will concentrate on. I mention these considerations here because your approach to the subject should be clearly defined before you begin to teach it.

Principles

1. ALLOW ENOUGH TIME.

A major pitfall in searching is a failure to allow enough time to obtain the papers selected. From the time the title and source are submitted to the librarian it may take from two weeks to six months to obtain the text. Even more time must be allowed if translation is required. The practical value of Assignment 5, below, is that it may impress a student with the need for timing his requests for literature.

2. VERIFY. VERIFY. VERIFY.

As a cardinal principle of search, emphasize how important it is to verify sources. You may wish to quote Place (1) on verification, in association with Assignment 6, (p. 177):

"A common fault lies in taking a reference from another's bibliography as though it were thereby Gospel truth. . . . Take no reference for granted. Verify the reference that your best friend gives you. Verify the reference that your revered chief gives you. Verify, most of all, the reference that you yourself found and jotted down. To err is human, to verify is necessary."

3. SHARPEN THE QUESTION.

Help students learn to be clear and precise about the subject of search, its limitations, the period to be covered, the sources of probable interest, and the eventual use of the information. Teach them to specify such details as:
    languages they will read;
    organism by sex and age;
    medications (if applicable) with dose limits in quantity, frequency, and
        duration;
    geographical boundaries of the research or applications;
    population;
    publication years;
and, perhaps, specific sources.

Discuss well-defined projects, such as methods for a patent search, obtaining a reference for a particular statement, organizing an annotated bibliography, preparing a critical review, or seeking an indicator organism as a basis for experiment.

Demonstrate, with a few case histories, that sources of literature (libraries and source books) are not necessarily organized to produce specific answers to specific questions.

Discuss the effect of the *phrasing of the question* ("Is water desalination practical?" versus "What was published in 1966 on desalination costs?") and the *nature of the resource* (the Library of Congress versus the *New York Times Inaex*) on the quantity and relevance of information that may be retrieved. Contrast a search for a cure for scurvy or for the melting-point of a synthetic derivative with a search for treatment of hypertension.

ASSIGNMENT 1

Let each student frame a question for library search and prepare either an annotated bibliography or a set of quotations, with reference to the sources. It will be desirable to limit the bibliography or note collection to one that can be compiled in one to two hours, based on literature indexed in one year.

Discuss the effectiveness of the questions, preferably with the assistance of an experienced librarian. Explain the process of negotiating the question with the librarian as an important phase of search, so that students will realize that the librarian is trying to be helpful when the question is reviewed. Urge students to pose questions that represent their real interests, not mere exercises (see Assignment 4).

Authorities agree that note-taking and the recording of sources is essential to literature search, but they do not agree on the best method of keeping these records. Some prefer cards, 3 x 5 or 5 x 8 inches; some prefer notebooks, loose-leaf or otherwise; some like loose paper slips; some use pens of various colors; some photocopy the text.

Assignment 2

Propose that, after a week or so of browsing, students bring in their notes and compare methods of note-taking, including the form of citation (see Assignment 4).

4. Know Your Sources.

It may be helpful to consider the literature in three categories: encyclopedic, including directories, bibliographies, handbooks, reference tables, and various kinds of dictionaries; books or monographs, including manuals, guides, textbooks, reviews, and reports of special commissions; and collections of articles, including primary journals and proceedings of conferences and symposia.

A well-selected list of encyclopedic sources, books, and basic journals, can have practical value to the graduate student, but stress selection for relevance, currency, and accessibility. (A selected bibliography of medical reference works, 1679–1966, distributed by the Medical Library Association, contains more than 2700 titles.)

Many university scientists collaborate with a librarian to identify and obtain the search aids most useful to their departments. The librarian, in turn, can introduce graduate students to the sources currently available and to their limitations and uses.

(If a librarian is available, this is a good spot for a guest lecturer on the resources of the local library for scientific investigations. Ideally, the talk should be in the library itself, where each reference source may be examined and the other facilities may be used.)

Trelease puts the use of the library at the forefront of the process of scientific research (pp. 3–11) and follows with a course of action for exploring the literature (pp. 11–25). In logical order, he prescribes (a) textbooks and monographs, (b) reviews (the National Library of Medicine publishes an index of medical reviews), (c) yearbooks or similar works, (d) abstract and index journals, (e) current literature, (f) original articles, and (g) guides to the literature, which he lists for respective scientific disciplines in the succeeding ten pages.

To this course of action, one may add the possibility of obtaining special bibliographies for the topic under review, sometimes by automated printout. The "demand bibliographies" obtainable from MEDLARS provide an example (Medical Literature Analysis and Retrieval Service, details given in *Guide To MEDLARS Services*, National Library of Medicine, Bethesda, Md.).

A classic on the approach to using reference materials is Mudge's introduction to Winchell's *Guide to Reference Books*, 6th and 7th editions. Mudge proposes a series of steps for the reader who desires to learn the intelligent use of reference books. These steps include:

1. Examine title page carefully for information as to:
   a) scope of work as indicated in title
   b) author's name
   c) author's previous record
   d) publisher
   e) date (while dates of copyright or preface do not guarantee the date of the information in the book, they help to place it, especially if they are earlier than the date of publication)
2. Read preface or introduction for:
   a) further information as to scope
   b) special features claimed
   c) limitations, if any
   d) comparison with other books on the same subject
3. Examine book itself for:
   a) arrangement
   b) kind of entry
   c) cross references, i.e., the extent to which these are included, and whether they are given in the main work or in a separate list

d) supplementary lists, noting their number and kind and how they are connected with the main work
e) indexes, noting fullness and exactness of reference
f) quality and kind of articles (scientific, signed, impartial, documented. Trustworthiness and accuracy are fundamental to the value of the work.)

The full text of Mudge's advice warrants careful study.

5. EYE THE INDEX.

Even in allied disciplines, index headings differ. For example, ecology means one thing to a sociologist, something else to a biologist. An item listed under Toxins in one index may turn up in another only under Poisons. An earnest searcher does not give up after reviewing one heading but looks into other possible associations. Explain how the selection (quality) and number (depth) of index terms affect search and retrieval.

(If available, a professional indexer or other expert in library automation might be invited to tell what the user needs to know about using automated storage, searching, and retrieval techniques. The exercise on framing a question, above, was aimed at the usual manual search. A question intended for an automated search will need some special treatment.)

6. DISCRIMINATE.

A search should not dig into every title listed, but should concentrate on the items that promise to yield relevant data. Warn students that titles may be misleading and that the reputation of the author is often a better guide. At the same time, stress the importance, when the searcher turns into an author, of composing descriptive titles, especially to support automatic indexing and searching.

The exercise of discrimination is tied to the prescription to Sharpen the Question. Students may enjoy the experience of applying discrimination to the selection of references according to titles. Let us take an example. Given a choice of titles on Statistics, the reader seeking an introduction to the subject can only guess which of the following would be best to consult:

Introduction to Probability and Statistics
Handbook of Probability and Statistics with Tables
Introduction to Statistical Analysis

Statistical Analysis of Experimental Data
Introduction to Theory of Statistics

He may have more to go on if his interest in statistics is related to an animal experiment, as the following titles suggest:

The Design of Experiments
Statistical Methods for Research Workers
Statistical Methods Applied to Experiments in Agriculture and Biology

The following titles suggest special qualifications in themselves:

Mathematics Essential to Elementary Statistics
Say It With Figures
Graphic Charts Handbook
Handbook of Graphic Presentation
Statistical Sources
Statistical Tables for Biological, Agricultural, and Medical Research

In the first batch of titles given above, the reader's discrimination will be based less on the title than on appraisal of the author's position, publications, and reputation. The reader will also consider the book's recency and durability. An updated classic that has gone through many editions, for example, may be a better bet than a relatively untested modern work.

In the second batch, the third title is the most specific and will therefore be the one most quickly selected or discarded.

In the third batch, all depends on whether the reader is asking "What do I need to know to study statistics?" (title 1); "What are good methods of presenting statistics?" (titles 2–4); or "Where can I find a handy set of reference tables?" (titles 5, 6). Item 4 is the title that points most directly to methods of presentation, unless the reader happens to know that "Say It With Figures" is especially well regarded.

Assignment 3

Using bibliographies obtained in Assignment 1, let students identify the titles that appear most nearly suited to their interests. Have each student then report whether investigation confirms his expectations, title by title. Each may submit the results in tabular form, but the experience may also lead to some profitable discussion of both the selection and construction of titles.

7. Give Up In Time.

Pique or stubbornness may seduce a student into wasting hours in a search for a relatively inconsequential piece of information. Or he may pursue a study long after he has passed the point of diminishing returns. For some, a search may prove so attractive an occupation that the investigator is reluctant to leave it for the duties of the bench and desk. Searchers should recognize this deflection of aim as a potential danger and discipline themselves to ask at frequent intervals "Should I stop now?" Like the gold prospector, the searcher may be obsessed by the feeling that the big strike is under the next rock. But reason, and a calm assessment of the cost/benefit ratio of his endeavors, may rescue him from the psychological forces of compulsion and obsession.

8. Create a Useful Product.

Ideally, the bibliography gained by the search should consist of citations written neatly on cards suitable for filing. Entries should be legible enough for a typist to copy accurately. The form should be consistent, and the annotations explicit. (The current condition of titles suggests that a bibliography without annotations is less functional than a bikini without a girl.) The needs of the reader must be considered as well as those of the investigator, and when the bibliography is reproduced as part of a publication the citations must be both complete and accurate.

Assignment 4

Let students exchange the notes they made in Assignment 2 and then rate each other for legibility, consistency of form in citation, and quality of the annotations. This exercise should demonstrate the value of creating a useful product. Preparation of a useful bibliography could be assigned in association with other exercises.

Practices

So much for principles. What are actual practices? Some people dote on abstracts. Others are satisfied with nothing but the full text of the original papers, which they locate from an index, an announcement, references in other papers, or the latest *Current Contents*. Many a search is started with a personal conversation, and it broadens and deepens as its importance engages the questioner in hot pursuit. Through his library, a reader may ask for a bibliographical search at the National Library of Medicine. Or he may be content with the local library catalog, the indexes, the abstracting journals, and whatever else is at hand. He may try to evaluate a document by looking into *Science Citation Index* to see how much it is used as a reference. If he cares to know about current research, he can inspect the *Research Grants Index* or submit an inquiry to the Science Information Exchange. If he is stumped for an answer from the literature, he may consult the National Referral Center for Science and Technology at the Library of Congress or its directories, or he may find a helpful source in the *Directory of Special Libraries and Information Centers*, edited by A. T. Kruzas (Gale Research, Detroit, 1963).

ASSIGNMENT 5

It may be instructive for the student to keep a record of his specific library requests, the time required for a response, or the reasons for any lack of response. (Failures and delays in library responses have encouraged many institutions to purchase works on demand, rather than borrow from a central library, especially if the works are new. The saving in time and effort compensates for the cost of the purchase.) Analysis of the failures can guide the searcher in improving request procedures: he may discover that he has inadvertently given the wrong spelling of the author's name, such as Lawton for Lewton; that he has cited the wrong journal—*Chemical Education* instead of *Chemical Documentation;* that he has erred on the date or volume number; that his script is easily misread; or that certain sources are in such heavy demand that it is futile to try to borrow them. Such practical experience is essential for evaluation of the precepts cited above. It also encourages a realistic approach to the art of searching.

ASSIGNMENT 6

The fallibility of man is such that, with the best of intentions, even a good scientist may misquote or misrepresent. Authors as well as readers should feel an obligation to check the sources. It will be a good learning experience for students who have written papers to review the papers and books given in their references and check them critically against their text. Alternatively, each student can be assigned to check the references in a scientific paper he has read: he may be asked to report on the accuracy of the citations, the accuracy of the quotations or interpretations, the availability of the literature cited, and the average time required to check a reference.

Summary

Search strategy copes chronically with tactical, practical obstacles. In theory, search may saturate the whole human experience. Narrowed down to an investigation of the open literature, search tends to funnel through a single essential portal: the facilities of a scientific library. Skill in using these facilities is acquired by study of the resources and practice in handling them.

In general, students may benefit from help in sharpening their questions, learning reference aids and other sources, studying indexing forms, discriminating among sources, rationing time, and aiming at a useful product. In the main, however, teachers should remember that the student will learn to swim only when he is wet. Once he is persuaded to leap into the library, he will make many random, wasteful efforts. He may even be in danger of drowning in the literary flood unless he is carefully coached in the art of identifying, selecting, screening, and searching the literature. The proper coaching can save his scientific life.

REFERENCE

1. Place, F., Jr. 1916. "Verify Your References." *New York Medical Journal.* 104: 697–9. (Note: the name of this journal was later changed to *New York State Journal of Medicine.*)

BIBLIOGRAPHY OF
FURTHER READING

You should, in the first place, become thoroughly acquainted with all the books given on p. 56 as the students' reading list. Because you are interested in writing you will enjoy the outstanding books by Quiller-Couch, Gowers, and Lucas, and will wonder why they have not been required reading for the students. The reason is that they deal in depth with literary style, which as we have seen is not an essential part of scientific writing. One aim of the teacher of scientific writing should be, we believe, to deemphasize the stylistic element, which has been overstressed in the student's past and is too easily dismissed by him as of minor importance—unfortunately, too often, along with all other considerations in writing. Tichy's book is less likely to antagonize the determined anti-literary student, and her Chapters 2, 3, 5, and 6 will neatly underline and amplify what you have had to say about organizing.

At the head of most chapters is a reading list of special interest to you in teaching that chapter. These references are not repeated here. What follows is a short list of titles you may like to dip into for further reading and use as sources of examples.

Recommended

Graves, Harold F., and Lyne S. S. Hoffman. 1965. *Report Writing*. Prentice-Hall, Englewood Cliffs, N.J., and London 4th ed.

Concerned largely with technical and business reports, which have somewhat different requirements from scientific articles, this book nevertheless has a good style chapter that is applicable to scientific writing. The chapter closes with exercises—sentences and paragraphs to be revised—which might form useful assignments.

Harrison, James (ed.). 1965. *Scientists as Writers*. The M.I.T. Press, Cambridge, Mass.; Methuen, London.

Like most anthologies in the field, this one is composed of pieces of *science* writing, i.e., writings by scientists for nonscientist readers. It may broaden your students' perspective and it will show them what good straightforward expository style is, but it will not teach them to write a journal article. The excerpts are thoughtfully commented on by the authors.

Jones, Everett L., and P. Durham. 1961. *Readings in Science and Engineering.* Holt, Rinehart and Winston, New York and London.

Similar to Harrison, see above.

Jones, W. Paul. 1965. *Writing Scientific Papers and Reports.* Wm. C. Brown, Dubuque, Iowa. 5th ed.

This book is intended as a text for an undergraduate course in scientific writing, and as such does not attempt to introduce the student to full-scale scholarly publication. "The intention is rather to confront students with a number of simple problems in scientific exposition and to give them instruction and practice in organizing ideas and communicating them to the reader." Teachable discussions of scientific method and logical thinking come, appropriately, at the beginning of the book and an excellent chapter (Chapter 19) on sentence structure and diction, appropriately, at the end.

Chapter 19 will provide you with a wealth of material either for individual guidance or for classes on Grammatical Refinements. If you are cajoled into giving these take, for example, Jones's basic classification on parallelism and balanced sentences, teach your students to use them correctly, and then widen their horizons by showing them examples (from Lucas, Graves and Hodge, or the anthologies by Harrison or Jones and Durham) in which the writer has used parallel constructions not only correctly but triumphantly.

Jordan, Archibald C. 1966. *The Writer's Manual (the Grammar and Mechanics of the English Language).* The World Publishing Co., Cleveland and New York.

This grammar is clearly and logically set out and its explanations are also clear and logical. As in any book on writing, the reader encounters usages that seem to him less than impeccable, for instance the example of a dangling past participle:

> Consumed in excessive amounts of more than 10 per cent of the ration, poultry specialists said that very young chickens die of some unknown cause.

is "corrected" to:

> When feed is consumed in excessive amounts of more than 10 per cent of the ration, poultry specialists said that very young chickens die of some unknown cause.

—a barely perceptible improvement. But in general the examples are good, and illustrate each point cogently. The book is to be recommended for those students whose grammar is weak, because although it is essentially simple and clear it does not "talk down" to the reader. The distribution of sections and subsections in an almost tabular arrangement will appeal to the scientist.

Two serious omissions limit the book's value as a reference manual: there is no index, and although the list of Contents is well set out, only the page numbers for the beginning of each chapter are given. The delay in finding particular points that those omissions occasion may well send the frustrated writer to another source of information.

Kapp, Reginald O. 1948. *The Presentation of Technical Information.* The Macmillan Co., New York; Constable, London.

The preface is excellent, in that it describes the deterrent suggestions encountered by one who proposes to teach scientific writing.

"I was told, for instance, that the whole of the ground ought to be covered at school. I was also advised to abandon the idea of a special course in presentation and, instead, to use the laboratory reports as basis for training the students in the art of exposition, going over each student's report with him sentence by sentence.

"These suggestions revealed a serious under-estimation of the magnitude of the problems that the executive engineer or scientist has to solve in the course of his professional work when he is presenting technical information or reasoned argument. These problems simply do not arise in such elementary factual statements as are contained in a student's laboratory reports. They are not problems in grammar and syntax. They are rarely problems in literary style. They are most often problems in logic and psychology. Teach a man to think clearly, and he is likely to express himself clearly; teach him to think about the person addressed, and he will have learnt the first lesson in the art of conveying information effectively from mind to mind. But teach him only to turn out well-constructed sentences and he may fail badly in the art of exposition."

In the four lectures that follow, the author teaches elementary logical and psychological principles in terms of a metaphorical storekeeper keeping watch over the brain or memory in which information is stored. This method of teaching fails to have lasting impact, however, because it is not related closely enough to the students' everyday activity; it is not linked to enough specific examples; and it does not demand the students' participation. It can succeed only if the teacher commands a language like Quiller-Couch's, so that the lectures are enjoyed at the time, and read frequently afterwards, for their literary excellence and their gusto. Dr. Kapp does not have this command, and so the text is a little flat. Although the author is distinctly on the side of the angels, therefore, his harp playing is not going to ravish and reform the renegade scientific writer.

Rathbone, Robert R. 1966. *Communicating Technical Information.* Addison-Wesley Publishing Co., Reading, Mass., and London.

Short and lively, the book iterates main principles in the name of communicating ideas instead of merely writing them down. The author may provide you with many vivid devices for making your students remember the principles you are trying to convey. Excellent further reading is suggested at the ends of chapters and in the annotated bibliography.

The author has forced the titles of all the chapters into a single form beginning with the definite article: let the resultant artificiality be a warning to you not to resort to such "cute tricks" in teaching. Graduate students in science believe that life is real and earnest, and they do not appreciate the kind of approach in which "The Inadequate Abstract" and "The Improper Introduction" are succeeded, apparently purely for esthetic reasons, by "The Ubiquitous Noise" and "The Neglected Pace."

Richards, Paul I., and Irving T. Richards. 1965. *Proper Words In Proper Places*. The Christopher Publishing House, Boston. Revised ed.

A well-written reiteration of the necessity for thinking and planning before writing. "*Part 1*: Strategy" in particular may provide reinforcement, if this should be needed, of the principles behind the early steps in writing a journal article.

Walsh, J. M., and A. K. Walsh. 1959. *Plain English Handbook*. McCormick-Mathers, Wichita, Kansas. Revised ed.

Together with the workbook *Plain English 12*, this constitutes a review course in English, intended for high-school seniors but useful for students who still have real difficulty with the language.

Weisman, Herman M. 1962. *Basic Technical Writing*. Charles E. Merrill Books, Inc., Columbus, Ohio; Prentice-Hall, London.

A thorough treatment suitable for a specialist planning a career as a technical writer. The chapters on Scientific Method and Approach; Technical Style, Mechanics, and Grammar; Graphic Presentation; and The Technical Article and Paper will be of special value to you. A wealth of examples of complete papers and their revision is provided. The tone throughout is direct and unpretentious, but the author cannot conceal his depth of scholarship.

West, Michael, and P. F. Kimber. 1958. *A Deskbook of Correct English*. Longmans, Green, London.

An excellent guide and easily consulted reference book for words and phrases commonly misspelled or misused; it can be highly recommended to students with difficulties of this kind.

Woodford, F. Peter. 1967. "Sounder Thinking through Clearer Writing." *Science*. 156:743–745.

A diatribe against the low standard of writing currently found acceptable in scientific journals, and a plea for graduate courses in scientific writing such as the one you are planning to give.

Others

Barnett, Lincoln. 1964. *The Treasure of Our Tongue*. Alfred A. Knopf, New York; Secker and Warburg, London.

A collection of extended articles originally published in *Life*, this book includes a brief history of the English language, its increasing use as a world language, and contributions to it from other languages. It ends with an eloquent plea for increased precision and careful use of the language in the future.

The book is gracefully and colorfully written, if a bit long-winded and repetitive. Because of the latter qualities it should not be required reading, but might earn a place on the Extra Reading list. Students could be referred in particular to the passage in the last chapter concerning Webster's Third Dictionary that leads into a description of the battles between "prescriptive" and "decriptive" grammarians.

Bernstein, T. M. *Watch Your Language*. 1958. Channel Press, Great Neck, N.Y.

This is a collection of squibs originally intended for limited circulation in the *New York Times* newsroom. It is wittily written and pungently makes some useful points on circumlocution, colloquialisms, and pomposity. Because of its orientation to newspaper writing, it would be useful only as extra reading for interested students.

A few short essays could be used as colorful illustrations of single points, e.g.: "One Idea to a Sentence," pp. 111–121; and "Syntax," p. 135. On the other hand, whole chapters are concerned with copy editing, composition of headlines, and construction of lead sentences, which are not to your purpose.

Burch, George E. 1954. *Of Publishing Scientific Papers*. Grune and Stratton, New York.

An essay with illustrations, directed especially at medical writing, with sound and wise statements on what should constitute and what should justify scientific publication. The illustrations are not particularly witty (they were obviously designed as slides to accompany an address) and it is unfortunate that their inclusion, as well as the children's-picture-book format, tends to trivialize the message, which surely deserves more weight. Scientific writing is more important than this kind of easy fun would indicate.

Emberger, M. R., and M. R. Hall. 1955. *Scientific Writing*. Ed. by W. E. Britton. Harcourt, New York.

This well-known textbook is made up for the most part of long examples, which may be useful to you as illustrations. The text itself is on the pedestrian side.

Fishbein, Morris. 1957. *Medical Writing*. Blakiston Co., Toronto, 3rd ed.

This book is a sort of extended *Instructions to Authors* of the Journal of the American Medical Association. The points it makes about style and grammar are neither thoroughly illustrated nor trenchantly expressed. The examples are, naturally enough, narrowly medical in subject matter and not usable in a wider scientific context.

Kegel, C. H., and M. Stevens. 1959. *Communication: Principles and Practice*. Wadsworth Publishing Co., Inc., San Francisco.

Unobjectionable, but long. The treatment is general, and yet it is too detailed for the scientist; the intellectual level is well below that of the graduate student.

Morris, Jackson E. 1966. *Principles of Scientific and Technical Writing*. McGraw-Hill, New York and London.

The main emphasis of this book, despite the form of the title, is on technical writing, although Chapter 12 deals, necessarily briefly, with scientific papers and theses. The level is more undergraduate than graduate and the stress more on the physical than the biological sciences. It may be useful as a source of special material.

Robertson, W. S., and W. D. Siddle. 1966. *Technical Writing and Presentation*. Pergamon Press, Oxford.

A short paperback for rank beginners, this book places its main emphasis on the writing of technical reports. Everything it has to say is clear and correct, but the science graduate will find its advice on the actual planning and construction of the writing too meager. On certain technical aspects of copying, printing, and construction of figures some useful and little-known facts are given.

SUBJECT INDEX

NAME INDEX